The Mississippi Bubble

THE MISSISSIPPI BUBBLE

---

by **THOMAS B. COSTAIN**

Illustrated by **WARREN CHAPPELL**

RANDOM HOUSE · NEW YORK

Contents

The Mississippi Bubble

ONE

A New Empire for France

1

A GROUP OF INDIANS WAS BUSY FISHING IN THE MUD-
colored waters of the Mississippi River. Their wooden
canoes were hidden by the dense grasses and cane-

brakes of the shore. Their watchful, keen eyes spotted strangers coming down the river long before the travelers saw them. As the big loaded birch-bark canoes of the latter came close, the fishermen leapt into their boats and struck out for their village downstream.

They paddled swiftly. Every bronzed back strained to make the canoes skim through the water. Never before had they witnessed such a strange sight. In the big oncoming canoes there were men whose faces shone deadly white in the morning sun. They wore a great deal of clothing, unfamiliar and curious garb. Some had hair on their faces and some were completely robed in black. The fishermen fled in terror.

A few of these savages had heard tales of the men with the chalk-white faces but not one of them had ever seen a white man. They knew all the delta country around them by heart—the low coastal plains, the numberless bayous and the sweep of the river as it neared the Gulf of Mexico. But none of them knew how big the valley of their river was, nor did they know there was an even bigger world beyond it belonging to the white man.

By swift steady strokes of the paddle the Indians

reached their village in a matter of minutes. Immediately the war drums began to beat out a warning. Soon the warriors were stealing out to the water's edge, well hidden in the tall grasses, each man supplied with arrows.

The white men in the approaching boats were not surprised to hear the drums of war. The leader of the party, Robert Cavelier, Sieur de La Salle, had been warned that there were at least ten different tribes along the shores of the Mississippi toward its mouth. These Indians were said to be warlike and barbarous. He had found, however, that many of the savages who lived along the river were not as fierce and hostile as those of the North.

Time after time he had been welcomed to native villages; there was often an elaborate ceremony when he was presented to the chieftains. He and his men were feasted—not for one day but for several—and the Indians asked them to join in the dance of the calumet to seal their friendship.

The natives liked La Salle. He was dignified and soldierly. This impressed them very much; and he had such an easy, friendly manner that he won their con-

5

fidence. He was so generous with his presents that they were sure the white man came as a brother. When he talked about France and his king, it was not too difficult for him to persuade them to share their country with the people of France.

In the land of the Arkansas and the Natchez La Salle and his companions had taken possession of this river country in the name of King Louis the Fourteenth. These rugged, fearless explorers carried out the proclamation for the King with as much ceremony and pomp as they could muster. This delighted the Indians and filled them with wonder. La Salle named the new empire Louisiana, in honor of Louis the Fourteenth. Now he was pressing on eagerly to the mouth of the river, undaunted by tales of the fierce tribes near the mouth. His goal was to reach the Gulf of Mexico and take possession of all the valley of the Mississippi for King Louis.

Many canoes had started out in La Salle's party of hardy French-Canadians and Indians on their journey to find a waterway to the west. The boats were loaded with fifty-four persons, muskets, ammunition and provisions for the months ahead of them; as much as they could pack into their boats and carry over the many portages they would have to make overland. There were women and children in the party. Some of the Indians who had agreed to guide La Salle refused to make the trip unless they could take their families with them.

The explorers had long since learned that the great river would not lead them west but to the south. Nevertheless they felt like conquerors as they moved on swiftly. They had traveled through many hundreds of miles of beautiful country, a land of forests and great plains and rivers teaming with fish. Around the campfire at night, they had talked about the wealth of it, imagining themselves rich from the gold in the mountains, or from the priceless furs.

It was clear to the intrepid La Salle and the members of his party that they were reaching their goal. The river had grown into a mighty stream, fed by the huge tributaries they had passed—the Missouri, the Ohio, and the Arkansas—and it rolled on now with majestic power. The signs began to multiply. The mouth of the Father of Waters had been described to them by friendly Indians farther north. There were three deep channels flowing through the islands of the mouth, the growth on the banks lush and abundant. Flowers, some familiar and some strange, made great splashes of color in the dazzling sunshine. The color and taste of the water would change as the explorers approached the end of their voyage.

The final sign now showed itself. The muddy and brackish water of the river was becoming fresh and green. Excitement grew in the long canoes. The men shouted and waved their hats. Some of them raised their muskets skyward and fired a volley in celebration of their success. The sound brought a panicky flight of birds which had been concealed in the grasses along the banks. They took to the air and the beat of their wings was like the rumble of war drums.

An answer came from the Indians hidden on the river bank. A shower of arrows was delivered from the safe shelter of the reeds. Most of them fell in the water but a few lodged in the sides of the canoes or whizzed by the white occupants. The *zing* of the speeding arrows could not be heard because real war drums were now beating farther back from the shore, and there was a menace in the sound which the droning wings of the birds had lacked.

The party of white men withdrew swiftly to the opposite shore and a council was held. Then a boat went out cautiously. They made signs of peace, holding up the calumet and calling out to the savages as friends. Once again a shower of arrows answered. The war drums became louder, more urgent.

La Salle had saved some of the finest gifts for these natives—knives and shoemakers' awls, beads, needles and tobacco. But he decided not to risk a closer approach to them. Orders were given for the boats to proceed, skirting the far shore.

And so they came to the place where the great river divided into three parts. La Salle chose the western channel; his favorite aide, Henri Tonti, took command of the center division; another lieutenant, D'Autray, took the east. It was La Salle's canoe which completed the journey first, bringing that ardent explorer within sight of the waters of the Gulf.

This was a time for celebration. The little party of hardy courageous men assembled on the shore. A pillar of oak was placed in the ground. On it was painted the Cross and the arms of the King of France. A leaden plate bearing a Latin inscription was buried at the foot of the pillar; the names of all of those who had taken part in the discovery were written on it.

In a loud, firm voice, La Salle took possession of this delta country, the river and all the valley it watered, every river that poured into it. He was an imposing figure in his gleaming breastplate and hat with white plumes. The men around him who had lived through perils and hardships with him raised their voices in the singing of *The Banners of Heaven's King Advance* and the *Te Deum*. This ninth day of April, 1682, was a day to be remembered.

2

Two years later La Salle set out again for the mouth of the Mississippi. This time he sailed direct from France with four ships, his purpose being to reach his destination by way of the Gulf of Mexico. King Louis had decided to back him in establishing a colony at the mouth of the river. France at that time was at war with Spain and there was a secret purpose back of the expedition. An army of Indians would be re-

In 1682 La Salle claimed Louisiana for France.

cruited and taken farther south to make war on the Spanish colonies. The French king hoped they would find and take over control of some of the gold mines which were making Spain rich.

It was a large expedition but ill fortune was with them from the start. Great storms scattered the flotilla and one of the ships was captured by the Spanish. When the three remaining vessels reached the Gulf they sailed off their course. La Salle had taken the latitude of the river mouth but had lacked instruments to enable him to take the longitude. The result was that they struck too far to the south, missing the mouth and finally locating at Matagorda Bay on the east coast of what is now Texas. Here he built a fort and set his people to work at clearing the land.

La Salle's ill luck was only beginning. He lost all his ships through disobedience of orders. There was only one thing left to do. He, La Salle, must set out for Canada on foot with the hope of getting word to France that the struggling colony would soon face starvation if help were not sent. While on the trip he lost his life. One of his own mutinous followers killed him with a musket shot from ambush.

King Louis the Fourteenth was enraged by the failure of the expedition. He refused to do anything about the unfortunate people stranded on the mud banks of Matagorda Bay and in a very short time they all died of starvation or were killed by hostile Indians.

Fifteen years passed and then the Sun King, as Louis was called by his courtiers, decided on another effort to establish a colony at the mouth of the majestic river. His purpose was not that of an explorer who will risk his life to search out the hidden places of the globe. There was instead a carefully considered plan in the minds of French leaders by which the Mississippi was to be lined with forts from its source to its mouth. This would close off the two nations contending with France for the new world, England and Spain. They would be locked within the relatively narrow space of the At-lantic seaboard while France would have all of the great West.

It was a bold scheme, the kind which appealed to the French monarch.

This time the King selected as his commander a great French-Canadian named Pierre le Moyne, Sieur d'Iberville.

Iberville was one of the greatest fighting men of all time. This may seem a rash statement in view of the fact that he has almost been forgotten. He fought in the battles between the French and the North American Indians and between the French and the English settlers, and few records were kept of what he did. The men who wrote the histories of that day were so absorbed in the wars the French were waging in Europe that they paid little attention to a backwoods hero.

Iberville was both a general and an admiral. He had led expeditions on foot through the endless miles of the northern woods, through marshes and over mountains and along rivers, and captured the English forts on Hudson's Bay in night attacks. Later he encountered three well-armed vessels on the Bay and had beaten them with one ship-of-war in a brilliant exhibition of naval daring. He had captured the colonies on Newfoundland in one brisk campaign. The Iroquois dreaded him, for he was ruthless as well as bold. His own people loved him and gloated over his exploits. "That Pierre, he can beat the old devil himself!" they said gleefully. His fame had even reached the court of the Sun King.

T W O

Ten Valiant Brothers

1

THE HERO OF NEW FRANCE (WHICH WOULD LATER BE called Canada) stood in the bow of the first of the two *chaloupes* battling their way across the stormy waters of the Gulf of Mexico. His men were striving desperately to keep the small vessels from driving upon a jutting point of black rock, and they were calling upon God to aid them. The leader, great Pierre le Moyne, who went by his title of Sieur d'Iberville, did not seem to share their concern. He was watching that line of rock intently, shading his eyes under one cupped hand. The wind blew his thick mop of yellow hair behind him in agitated ringlets. There was a look of expectancy rather than fear on his face.

He had left his fleet of three ships in the lee of an island off the Mobile River and had set out in the two *chaloupes* with the intention of hugging the shore in these lighter craft until they reached the mouth of the Mississippi. The storm had blown up suddenly while they were weaving a course through a cluster of islands. Now, almost without warning, they found themselves faced by a fantastic barrier which looked like a palisade of rock and tree trunks. With the wind behind them, they could not hope to swing around this formidable ledge. The members of the crew prayed to the Mother of Christ and all the saints to protect them.

Now the French *chaloupe* is a sturdy type of vessel capable of mounting a gun or two and accommodating a crew of two score men. It is a fine, dependable cobhorse of a boat. Iberville looked at the barrier ahead. It was made up, he was sure, of alluvial deposits, which means the mud and wood brought down year after year by the current of the river. The deposits grow layer after layer until they seem like walls of the strongest rock. Iberville knew that they were never as firm as they looked. He knew also the soundness of the timbers under his feet. He called out an order.

"Pull about! Drive straight on!"

For a moment his men wondered if the great Iberville had gone mad. Drive straight against this rock barrier? The boats would be smashed to matchwood, and every man of them would die in the raging waters.

But they believed in Iberville; and, moreover, they had been taught to obey. If he ordered them to drive head on against a reef with sharp teeth of rock, drive on they must. The tall man with the wild golden hair had always before been right. Perhaps he expected God to reach down a hand and save them all.

Theirs not to reason why. The two *chaloupes* were brought about. The gale took them and swept them on full astern.

Another order came from the calm man in the bow. "To the lee of the rocks! Steady, my men!"

The boats plunged forward and were caught up in a mountainous wall of water which threw them against the barrier. The barrier seemed to shudder and give. It broke up with the force of the impact. Now the boats were sliding through boiling water and debris. The wall, as Iberville had known, was not of rock but of mud baked black under the hot sun. It crumbled and let them through into calmer water.

After the first moment of shock and amazement, Father Douay, the priest with the party, cried out, "Look! The muddy water that La Salle himself talked about!"

Quickly, Iberville scooped up a handful and tasted it. The water was fresh! "Praise Heaven, we've found it! We've found the Mississippi!" As if by magic, the storm had driven them into the fresh waters of the great river.

Even so, as they toiled up the river some days later,

Pierre le Moyne, Sieur d'Iberville

awed by the strangeness, the chaos of reeds, of hideous monsters and eerie birds, they wished for some definite proof that they were ascending the mysterious stream which the Spaniards had aptly named the Hid River. It was this desire which kept Jean-Baptiste le Moyne, Sieur de Bienville, on a sharp survey of the terrain as they passed.

At this point it must be explained that Pierre le Moyne, Sieur d'Iberville, had nine brothers, raised at the family estate of Longueuil on the St. Lawrence River just above Montreal; and that all the brothers were valiant. Jean-Baptiste was the eighth of the line. He was a thin, scholarly lad of nineteen years, far different from his heroic brother, the strong Pierre. Why Iberville had selected him to come on the expedition has never been explained. It is possible he had seen the need for someone with good judgment, a cool head, and a shrewd eye for detail to serve under him. Bienville had these qualities in full measure.

At one point the young brother cried out excitedly. He thought he saw the remains of the great tree felled by La Salle and his party and hoisted up high in the form of a cross when they took possession of all this land.

"Look, Pierre! Over there! Doesn't that look like it? Like La Salle's pillar of oak?"

"Your imagination is running away with you, my little brother," said Iberville, smiling broadly. "Or is the sun playing tricks with your eyes? It is not La Salle's oak. But what of that? I don't need such proof to know that this is the Mississippi."

Jean-Baptiste's imagination *was* running away with him. In his mind he saw the little party of Frenchmen standing about the pillar, La Salle in his gleaming breastplate, the Indians standing about in a wondering group. He could almost hear the exultant voices raised in the *Te Deum,* the echo of muskets fired into the air, the shouting of *Vive le roi!*

"Better keep your eyes sharp for a site for the capital of our new colony, young Jean-Baptiste," said Pierre, recalling him from his vision.

"New Orleans!" Jean-Baptiste said the name that they had chosen. He was filled with awe, for his brother had promised to entrust him with the planning and founding of the new colony.

As the *chaloupes* passed by the shores heavy with the scent of wild peach and plum and garlanded by thick

21

flowering vines, they came upon a bend in the broad river. And with one accord the name of the new capital came to their lips again as they gazed upon a broad stretch of land high above the water, with hills in the background. It was the ideal site they had been hoping to find. It was ideal because it was far enough from the actual mouth of the river to have firm, high land and at the same time to be protected from damage by the winding river below it.

"I can see it already," cried Jean-Baptiste. "People going into the Cathedral—and the *Place d'Armes* over there! There will be tall spires and great bells tolling. And everyone will be rich."

Two weeks later they had the final proof of their discovery. It came about at the Indian village of the Bayougoulas. These Indian braves came forward to meet them, sounding for all the world like sleighs in a Quebec midwinter; for their belts were laden with bells and pieces of jangling copper. Iberville greeted them with their own gesture of welcome, gently rubbing his stomach. Bienville, who had a knack of picking up Indian dialects, found that he could understand them. The Chief, wearing only a single lock of hair bound in

22

many feathers, and a loincloth of moss, told them that it was indeed the mouth of the river.

When the Frenchmen presented the chief's people with mirrors and beads and hatchets, the Indians came forward with their presents. There were deer skins and corn bread and a gift that they put into Iberville's hands with great ceremony—the "speaking bark of the man with the iron hand." To Iberville's joy it was a letter written on birch bark by the Canadian explorer Tonti and left with the Indian Chief to be delivered to La Salle, whom Tonti had hoped to meet there. La Salle had never lived to find the river again and the brave Tonti, who had replaced a lost hand by an iron one, had had to retrace the three thousand miles through hostile lands back to Canada again.

"Now there can be no trace of doubt," Iberville told his little party that night in March, 1699. "We have found the water of the river that will some day wash the shores of France's great new empire."

Eagerly they turned southward then, back to their ships, wanting to get at their task of building a colony on the Gulf.

23

2

But many years were to pass before their dreams came true. The expedition had touched first at a place on the north of the Gulf which Iberville named Biloxi. They returned to Biloxi after their success in finding the mouth of the river and the commander decided that a fort should be built there. Temporarily it would serve as the headquarters of the French on the Gulf. The great city they hoped to build on the bend of the river would come later.

Iberville had chosen well. Biloxi Bay was a safe harbor, well screened by Deer Island. The bay extended back into the mainland for several miles and Deer Island lay across the mouth of the bay, blocking it off except for a channel at either end. This made a snug little harbor for the new settlement. There was always the danger of English or Spanish ships appearing on the green waters of the Gulf.

The site that the great leader chose for the fort was ideal. It was a high bank on the east side of the bay near the mouth. Here the French guns could sweep the horizon and the lookout could keep a sharp eye on the beach, the water, and the country round about. There were deep ravines on two sides of the hill which ran down to the bay; this made a natural fort of the hill. The weakest spot was on the forest side where the land sloped gently to the woods beyond. Iberville put his men to work immediately to build a strong entrenchment from one ravine to the other. He knew only too well how suddenly and swiftly the Indians could attack.

Here the Frenchmen labored like beavers. First the land had to be cleared. The trees were hard to cut. Most of them were oak or nut trees and so desperately hard that it would often take a whole day to bring one of them down. The hard-pressed men broke their axes in their haste to get the trees leveled. Forges had to be set up so that the axes could be mended. They had to build a strong wall behind which they could live.

The fort they erected was similar to those which the French had always constructed in their pioneering efforts along the St. Lawrence River. There were several wooden buildings, the main one two stories in height, inside a high barricade of logs. The outer wall had bastions at each corner. These were made of squared logs, two to three feet thick, placed one upon another.

The four bastions were surrounded by deep ditches, and they served as projections from which the defenders could meet the attacks of the enemy with raking fire in all directions. They could also keep the enemy from setting fire to the walls of the fort.

The fort was stoutly constructed, a wise thing because the country thereabouts was literally alive with Indians. Most of the party were French-Canadians and so the danger from Indian attacks was nothing new to them. Every French-Canadian had heard at some time that terrible, high-pitched screech of *Cassee Kouee!* with which the Iroquois braves went into action. They all remembered the massacre of Lachine, where a whole village had been wiped out by the men of the Six Nations.

But things were different here. The underbrush and vegetation were so much thicker than they had been accustomed to in the forests of the north that Indians could creep to within a few feet of the edge of the clearing without being seen or heard. The sentries could always be certain, as they stood guard on the walls, that many pairs of eyes were fixed on them from the thick screen. And while the Indians of the delta country—the Bayougoulas, the Quinipissa, the Moctobys, the Tensas, the Pascagoulas—were not more fierce or brave than the tribes of the north, they were sly and treacherous and with a brand of savagery all their own.

The men worked so quickly and with such industry that the fort was built within six weeks' time. Indians by the dozens came from miles around to watch the magic that the white men were performing with their swinging axes. They were amazed at the speed with which the land was cleared. They stood in awe of these white men who could fashion buildings so quickly out of timbers so big that it took twelve men to move one of them.

Of course these Indians came as guests and they had to be fed and presented with gifts. So many of them came that it grew to be a problem. The little colony did not have food to spare. Their supplies had to last until more ships came from France. Corn and peas were planted in the clearings, small crops that would not be ready to harvest for some time. They even had to ration the drinking water; it had to be carted to the fort from some distance. This was a life that was familiar to the French-Canadians and freebooters with the party. To the soldiers and sailors and laborers who came from France, it was a strange adventure.

While the fort was being built, the longboats were busy bringing supplies and equipment to the settlement. Iberville's ships were anchored at a roadstead several leagues away, in the lee of Ship Island. All the stores for the colony were dumped upon the silver-white sand of the shore and hauled up to the fort. Every man had to work hard. This was not what the French-Canadian liked—he preferred to hunt and fight.

Iberville, the great leader, was not fitted temperamentally for this kind of life. He was a man of action, equally at home on the sea or on the forest trail. To sit down in indolence behind a log palisade under a broiling hot sun and wait for the new colony to grow was foreign to his nature. Adventure beckoned him from the hot seas where the Spaniards held the power. After giving final instructions, he headed his ships out into the Gulf. So he left for France before the fort was completed, appointing a man named Sauvole as commander in his absence and his brother, Bienville, as first lieutenant.

It was a rare good thing for the slender and delicate

boy, Jean-Baptiste de Bienville, that he was thus left in a new land, where the thickets at night were filled with the calls of strange beasts, where alligators crawled up out of the water and slithered fearsomely around the palisade, and long black snakes twisted themselves around the sharpened tops of the logs in the wooden wall. He was being given the chance to become a great man at a very early age.

3

The father of the ten brothers was Charles le Moyne, a native of Normandy. He had emigrated to Canada as a young man and had established himself in the outpost of Montreal, the little town on an island where the Iroquois nearly always struck first. In the fullest sense the father was as great as his fabulous sons. Becoming well known as a scout and Indian fighter when quite young, Charles le Moyne was thoroughly hated and feared by the Iroquois braves. For years the old women of the Long House (a term sometimes applied to the Iroquois) had been gathering wood to burn him at the stake.

The brave Le Moyne was finally captured. The band of warriors who had surprised him somewhere on the Richelieu (a small river running north to the St. Lawrence) could hardly wait to take him back to the warm reception the old women had planned.

But they did not get that far. Charles le Moyne began to talk to them. He told them of the disasters and punishments which would come on them if anything happened to him. Great white armies would come to root them out. These armies would have canoes higher than the sides of a mountain and they would have guns longer than the trunks of the oldest trees. The guns would destroy the Iroquois villages, and the wrath of the white gods would not be satisfied as long as a single Iroquois remained alive.

He repeated his threats so often and with such gory details that the paddles began to dip more slowly. The bronze warriors were beginning to believe him. Slower and slower went the canoes. Finally they could not stand it any longer. They turned about and took him back to the place where they had caught him. They were glad to see the last of him.

Perhaps Jean-Baptiste de Bienville felt that he could

follow the example of his bluff and gallant father. At any rate he began to explore the whole of this wild country along the north shore of the Gulf and the course of the Mississippi. He did so without fear, sometimes with a small party at his back, sometimes alone. This lad of twenty, thin and delicate in health, did not hesitate to go anywhere. He traveled by canoe and on foot over the most difficult parts of the country, venturing boldly among the marshy bayous and into the densest and wildest of forests. He did this with all the courage his father had shown.

One of his chief feats was to cross from Biloxi to the Mississippi on foot, with just one companion, a man named Pennicaut. It was a dangerous mission but the two men came through it safely. Bienville had an extraordinary knack for picking up languages, and this was a great help to them. All he ever needed was a few weeks in the company of the men of a new tribe and he would understand what they were saying. In that time he might even be able to speak to them. The Indians had a habit of eking out their narrow vocabularies by using signs and gestures. The young French-Canadian was adept with his hands. He could talk with

31

strange tribesmen by twitching his fingers and motioning with his arms, and even more by the expressions on his face.

The trip across the portage from the Gulf to the Mississippi was made easier, therefore, by the fact that Bienville could talk with all the Indians they encountered. No matter how angry the natives might be at the start and how ready to have their scalping knives out, he could placate them with a smile, a nod of his head and an eloquent motion of his fingers.

He came back to headquarters from this trip with a firmer belief than ever that the colonizing of the delta country must center around a great seaport on the Mississippi itself. Reaching the bend of the river which Iberville had pointed out as the best site, he went over the ground carefully and decided how the city would be laid out when the time came to act.

Iberville came back to Louisiana on the eve of Twelfth Night in the year 1700. The weary men who had existed so long in the bare log huts behind the palisade, in constant peril and privation, lined the walls of the fort and cheered like mad while gunners fired a salvo of welcome. The great leader had done his best for them. He had new recruits on board, provisions, ammunition, money (to meet the back pay of the men), and even another of the Le Moyne brothers. This time it was the youngest of them, seventeen-year-old Antoine, who was called the Sieur de Chateauguay.

Antoine was due to live all his life in semi-tropical posts. He finally became the governor of French Guiana. There is no record of his death but it is believed he remained in harness to the end. When did he die? Was he married? Did he have children? The archives have no answers on any of these points. He may have been another Bienville, with the patience and administrative skill of the latter, but fated to do his work in obscurity.

On his next visit, Iberville had become convinced that another fort should be built on the Mobile River. He wanted it to be far from the mouth and this suggested a difficulty at once. The land through which the Mobile ran belonged to one of the most hostile tribes in the delta country.

Bienville said it would be advisable first to visit the Indians and get their consent. He volunteered to go himself.

"Do you remember what happened when that Spanish explorer, De Soto, went up the Mobile?" asked Iberville, looking anxiously at his younger brother.

Bienville said he did not know.

"He and his men were ambushed by Indians at a place called Mauvilla. Most of the Spaniards were killed or taken prisoners. I don't want to send you on as dangerous a mission as that."

Bienville was not afraid. He pointed out that it was more than a century since that incident had occurred. The Indians were seeing white men for the first time then. While they were still unfriendly, he did not believe they would be too hard to handle.

"If you go, you must have a large party with you," declared Iberville. "I can't let you throw your life away, Jean-Baptiste."

The younger brother pointed out that to take a large party would be to convince the Indians that they came with warlike intent. It would be wiser if he had only a few men in his party. Iberville finally agreed to have him attempt the mission with a single canoe and two companions. But he wore a look of deepest worry when he saw Bienville raise his paddle in farewell as the brave trio started off up the river.

34

It was rough and dark country through which the trio made their way, paddling vigorously to achieve headway against the current. They met some friendly Indians on the second day and were informed that the warriors knew of their coming and were arranging to give them a reception far from friendly. Bienville received this news with a serious frown but proceeded at once to make it clear that he intended to keep on.

"They don't know that we come to make peace," he said to his two companions. "We must risk it. If we turn now, we'll never be able to come back."

The lone canoe continued onward. Early on the third day, when they had journeyed over fifty miles, they turned a bend of the river and were confronted with a sight which would have chilled the blood of men less courageous. The surface of the river was covered with canoes, each filled with natives in full war paint.

The appearance of the little French party set the Indians off. Never before, perhaps, had such wild screeching been heard. The Indians threw themselves furiously to work with their paddles and in a matter of seconds the French canoe was surrounded. There was no escape for them if they had lost their courage at this critical moment. A menacing tomahawk was raised in

35

every bronzed hand. The noise was indescribable.

Bienville was saying to himself: "No Indian ever dared touch my father. Why should I have fear when he had none?"

He stood up in the canoe and raised his arms to show that he was without weapons. Fortunately, he knew a little of their language.

"Men of this great nation!" he cried. "I come to offer you peace and the friendship of the French. I bring with me gifts from the Great White Father of our people."

The Indians were astonished to hear their own language issuing from the mouth of this bold youth, this paleface who did not seem to know any fear. They waited for their chief to decide what was to be done. The latter, an old warrior whose head was almost concealed under a bonnet filled with long white plumes, brought his canoe alongside.

"Do white men wish to die?" he asked. "We want no dealings with white men. Fires are being built on shore for them."

Bienville proceeded then to follow the example his father had set so many years before. Did the men of this great nation, he asked, want to die too? Did they not know that armies of white men would come up the river to avenge them? Did they know that the war canoes of the white men were as high as the sides of a mountain? Had they no fear of the guns of the white men which were as long as the trunks of the tallest tree? Did they not know that the leader of the French was the boldest and bravest man who had ever lived and that he would scatter them with one blow?

His boldness had the effect he had expected. The chief consulted with some of his head men and found that their faith had been shaken. The outcome was that Bienville and his two followers were taken ashore, not to be chained to the stake and to have fires lighted under them, but to sit in council with the men of the Indian nation.

The Frenchmen spread blankets on the ground and covered them with the gaudy and tempting gifts they had brought. The eyes of the natives began to glitter with desire to possess what they saw.

"You could kill us now, great chief," declaimed Bienville, "but never again would the Great White Father send you gifts from his storehouse."

Greediness was now added to the fear of vengeance

and the Indians were convinced that it would be wise to receive the little party in peace. Bienville spent several days in long talks with the head men and in much smoking of pipes. The result was that they reached an understanding. The French were to give gifts many times greater in measure than what was displayed on the blankets. In return they would be allowed to set up their tents and live side by side with the Indians.

The tents that the French set up under this agreement took the form of a fort. It was named Fort Maurepas and it was strong enough to resist any attacks which might be launched against it. But the gifts were as many as the sands of the sea and, for a time at least, the warriors were content with their bargain.

Iberville's plan for a new fort turned out to be a good one. It had required the courage and wisdom of the younger brother, however, to make it possible.

Iberville came back for the last time in the winter of 1702. Sauvole had died in the meantime and all the responsibility had fallen on the thin shoulders of the youthful Bienville. He had brought about many improvements. The men had been put under sterner discipline and were no longer allowed to make free with

Bienville offered gifts to the Indians.

the brandy. The forts were in good condition, the guards on the walls were alert, the guns were kept primed and ready. Content with the way things were going, the greatest of the ten brothers sailed away—and never came back.

4

All that is known of the death of Iberville is that it occurred in the year 1706 in Havana. He had been taken down with yellow fever and was moved ashore. There are no records but it may be assumed that he was placed in quarantine and passed away there. It is not known where he was buried.

This is not the kind of end a hero should have. But Iberville alive was never given the measure of praise his great deeds had earned. He was always a hero to his countrymen in Canada but in France he was no more than a rough woodsman to the polished gentlemen who controlled the destinies of the country.

He was too young to die, a mere forty-four. His best years were ahead of him and if he had been allowed to live longer he might have become a world figure. Such were the thoughts, no doubt, which ran through his mind as he tossed on his rough pallet. One thing only is certain about the ending. The great Canadian, who had always loved company and was gay and exuberant with his companions, died alone.

Bienville remained in command in Louisiana for eleven years after his brother died. Sometimes supply ships arrived from Canada or France. Sometimes none put in an appearance and the colonists lived for months and years on the food they could raise. The men received no pay and finally reached the stage where they had to dress in skins like a company of Robinson Crusoes. Sometimes there were floods which wiped out the crops. Always there was the terrible heat.

They fought continuously against the Indians—the warlike Alabamas, the Choctaws, the Chickasaws. They had to guard against the aggressions of the Spanish and the English who did not want them to have possession at the mouth of the Mississippi.

The hardest of all to bear was the lack of news from home. They sometimes went for years without hearing anything from the outside world. Needless to state, they went wild with joy whenever a ship appeared in the Bay, flying the flag of France.

All that Bienville had to support him during these years of trial was the dream which had driven La Salle on to his continuous efforts and which the Le Moyne brothers had shared later. The young commander could remember the talks between the tall brothers when they got together in the family chateau at Longueuil. They had talked of winning all America for France, particularly the seemingly endless plains which stretched westward from the Mississippi. It had always been clear to the Le Moynes that the way to win was to hold the line of the Mississippi. And that was what he, Bienville, was doing.

But now it seemed that nothing less than a magic wand waved over the Mississippi could make it the vital, thriving empire that La Salle had conceived, the dream that filled the eager minds of the ten brave brothers.

THREE

Enter John Law

1

TWENTY YEARS LATER THERE WAS A MAN IN FRANCE
who waved the magic wand. But he was not French—
he was a young Scotsman named John Law. He was

destined to put magic into the name Mississippi, to set all France mad and the whole world talking, to make all men first rich and then poor.

John Law was an astonishing fellow. The son of a banker and goldsmith in Edinburgh, he was raised as a gentleman and became in his early twenties a fop, a gambler, a ruffler always ready to resort to the sword at his side, a man of such amazing good looks that he fascinated all the ladies. As a result of his high temper and ready skill with the sword, he killed a certain Beau Wilson in a duel early one morning in Bloomsbury Square, London. Arrested and sentenced to death, he managed to escape and fled the country. With him he took his beautiful young wife, Lady Catherine Knollys, who was a member of the British nobility, and the two children they had brought into the world.

For a number of years Law traveled on the continent, not as a poor fugitive but as a fine gentleman of fortune. He was extravagantly dressed and always ready to gamble, with cards, with dice, or at the wheel. His luck was supposed to be phenomenal but his winnings were the result of his cool knowledge of odds combined with almost incredible daring.

44

Those who knew John Law intimately and had his
confidence knew a different John Law. They knew that
all the while he had been traveling the country with
his wife and children, outwardly amassing a fortune by
gambling, he had been deep in the study of finance and
commerce, subjects that had long obsessed him. When
in Holland he studied the operation of the famous bank
of Amsterdam. He developed all sorts of schemes that
might fill the empty coffers of a country, and these
he took back to his native land where they were rejected.
He offered his services to other countries and nowhere
could he discover a government ready to listen. He
remained convinced that his plans would work. In the
meantime he was developing his theories into a con-
crete *system*, one that would make a nation rich.

He was in many countries and always they yielded
their gold to him at the gambling table but refused to
do anything but laugh at his theories. He was in France
once, in the latter days of Louis XIV, and tried to present his schemes to that old autocrat. Louis had listened
to many wild schemes in his time, and had lost money
on all of them, but he refused to hear Law because
the Scot was a Huguenot, a Protestant. The police saw

to it that this suspicious character was escorted out of the country.

Then in 1715 the old king died and Law returned to France; and with his arrival began the wildest, maddest, the most fantastic boom the world has ever seen.

2

Louis XIV had died and his great-grandson, who succeeded him, was only five years old. The Duke of Orleans was appointed regent. Now the Duke was a man of some ability and of good intent in the main, but he was also a rake and of a sufficiently giddy disposition to gamble with the security of the nation. The old king had spent so much money on his wars and his great palaces and the glittering court he kept about him that France was on the point of tottering over the edge into bankruptcy. Sincerely anxious to save the country, the regent listened to the eloquent and convincing tongue of that Scottish wizard who believed he could do the trick by waving a wand—John Law.

John Law's scheme was revolutionary but to the Duke of Orleans it seemed plausible enough. In brief, Law advocated the formation of a royal bank which was to manage the trade and currency of the country, to collect the taxes and, if necessary, to issue paper money. The last-named function was the nub of the scheme. France lacked the gold to pay off the national debt, so why not set the printing presses working and pay them with paper bills?

The regent considered the plan. Paper money! A capital idea. Had it not been tried out already in New France? Yes, answered Law, it had, and most successfully. An obscure but ingenious fellow named M. de Meules, having no gold handy, had conceived the idea of paying the soldiers with sections of playing cards stamped with the royal seal and his own signature. This form of payment had been used off and on ever since, and no one gave it a thought. Of course, the playing cards had always been redeemed with gold rather promptly.

Perhaps it should be explained here that paper money has no value in itself although the whole world has become accustomed to it. In earlier days money had to be made of metal—gold or silver or copper. The coins were worth whatever was marked on the surface. When paper money is issued, the government must have sufficient gold in the treasury to redeem every bill if necessary. The fact that a person can walk into a bank and demand coins to the full value of a bill is what gives the paper bill its value. It is a promise on the part of the government to pay in gold or silver the full amount stamped on the face of the bill.

There have been times when governments have issued more paper money than they could redeem in gold and the result has always been the same. People have lost faith in the paper currency and have refused to accept it. In the end it has always become practically worthless.

The regent knew all this. He was aware that issuing paper money was dangerous when the treasury was bare of gold. Still, something had to be done because France had heavy debts and almost no gold to pay them. The regent finally gave his approval.

There were others who did not approve. The Council of France said "No," loudly and emphatically. They did not want paper money. Law was not to be beaten by a lot of old-fashioned bankers. He advised the regent that they could get their way gradually in spite of all this opposition.

The first step taken was the granting on May 2, 1716,

of permission to Law to open a private bank and to issue paper bills. This institution was such an immediate success that two years later it was converted into a state bank and all limitations on the issue of paper money were withdrawn. The people were all in favor of the Law idea by this time.

It would be tiresome to trace all the steps whereby Law attained power over business and finance in France. He came in the course of two years to have a tobacco monopoly, the control of an Eastern concern called the Company of Senegal, and his own company for the development of a new empire in America called the Company of the Mississippi and the Occident. This last was what he had aimed at from the beginning, an opportunity to reap the wealth of the great unknown land west of that great sluggish river, the Father of Waters, for the exclusive benefit of France. He knew that the enormous and still mysterious river rolled through land that was undeveloped, which gave no promise of gold or precious stones or spices, in fact none of the easy wealth which the East supplied. He seems to have been convinced, however, that out of this unpredictable country would come wealth. He counted upon Louisiana to provide substance for the stocks he was issuing.

People were beginning to scramble for shares in his company. A boom was starting.

Every American knows what a boom is because we have had so many of them. The one which comes first to mind is the stock market boom of 1929. Men had become convinced then that the United States was always going to have prosperity and that there would be an increasing market for goods. This meant that all companies would continue prosperous and their stocks would be increasingly valuable. People rushed to the market to buy stocks. Generally they bought on margin, which meant that they paid down only a certain part of the price. Some transactions were even on a ten-per-cent margin. The boom became so mad that many stocks reached prices three or four times greater than their real value. As many as five million shares were sold each day on Wall Street and it took hours after the market closed to record all the transactions.

Finally, of course, common sense asserted itself and people stopped buying shares at these fantastic prices. The market "broke." Prices went down. In three days they fell lower than their real values. All who had bought on margin—and that meant hundreds of thousands of people in all parts of the country—were ruined.

Black days followed the breaking of this boom. It took ten years for the country to recover from the effects of it.

There have been booms in other things besides stocks. There have been real-estate booms and gold booms. Several centuries ago there was even a boom in tulip bulbs in Holland, during which the price of rare bulbs went as high as five thousand dollars!

This was what was now happening in France.

3

While the Mississippi bubble formed, there was no day more thrilling for John Law than that of August 27, 1719. He was to appear during the morning before the Regent. Word had long since gone around Paris that Law had another project, one that would further strengthen his hold on the country's finances. The Court buzzed with rumor and gossip. "It is preposterous—the man is mad!" stormed those who were against him. "Is there anything left for him to take over?" cried the incredulous. Paris was waiting with curiosity and suspense.

51

John Law was aware of the tension, but not in the least disturbed. He dressed that day with more than ordinary care, his keen dark-gray eyes watching every move of his valet's busy fingers. His full-skirted coat must hang with perfect grace. Every detail of his elegant costume from his flowing wig to the highly polished leather shoes with their high heels must be just so. He hummed with nonchalance as he admired the tiny gold buttons that decorated the full length of his embroidered coat.

His brother, William Law, his co-worker and confidant, was far from light-hearted. He paced back and forth in his brother's chamber as he waited for the time of departure to the Palais Royal. He admired his brother's genius, the brilliant eager mind that had conceived of ways to take over the entire economy of France. He believed in his great Company, yet he could not help but think of the gamble, the risk that was involved; for when John Law had established the Company, representatives of the King had insisted that shares of the Company be subscribed for in State notes. This was an excellent way of getting rid of a huge mass of worthless paper that had been issued by Louis the Fourteenth. These had fallen in value.

As if reading his brother's mind, John Law began to talk, with his heavy Scottish accent. "It can be done, my dear William, one tremendous Company encircling the whole of France to make a new rich France!"

His fingers moved slowly down the row of gold buttons edging his coat, as if he were counting his assets and reveling in it.

"My private bank is now the Royal Bank. My Mississippi Company gives me twenty-five years to reap a fortune, all the profit from all commerce and resources, all the beaver trade of Canada. The right to make war on the Indians and the granting of lands, raising of forts, selection of the governor——" his fingers moved on and on, "——Of course I must send six thousand people —but everybody wants to go to the Mississippi."

This was one of his greatest miscalculations. Nobody wanted to go to Louisiana. The home loving people of France were only too eager to share in its wealth but they had no desire to encounter the hardships and dangers of a pioneering life.

William Law, seated now and staring out of the window, seemed to carry out his thought by murmuring, "Some believe that you have enough power, now that

53

the Regent has given you control over the mint!"

The brothers looked at each other for a moment, knowing how possible it was for the Regent, with his love of the extravagant, to make this a threat. John Law's idea of credit and the printing of paper money had come like a gift from Heaven to the Regent when a bankrupt France weighed heavily on his shoulders. There was always the danger now that he would overstep the mark, ignoring John Law's unshakable principle that gold must always be there equal to the demand.

John Law was quick to shake off this thought.

"Yes, the mint—and the Government shall have the consideration promised. I shall deliver to the king the sum of fifty million livres within fifteen months. Never fear, my brother!"

He smiled as he picked up his three-cornered hat and surveyed himself in the mirror for the last time. France was going to be shaken before the end of the day. His final proposal was to be laid before the Regent. With the power he wrought he would bring gold to France— gold, streams of gold, rivers of gold as wide and steadily flowing as the great Mississippi in his empire of Louisiana.

John Law became the financial king of France.

Philippe d'Orleans, Regent of the realm, looked very much like his late uncle, who had been called the Sun King. He was proud of this resemblance and strove to dress in ways which accentuated it. It was not the impeccably attired figure that the court knew best, however, who greeted the visitor. To keep his appointment with the spectacular Scot, he had hurriedly left the chemical laboratory where he idled away much of his time. There he conducted or watched experiments which he hoped (or so people whispered) would give him knowledge of forbidden things—the Philosopher's Stone, the Elixir of Life, the power to summon the Prince of Darkness to his aid. The stains of chemicals had been carefully removed from his hands when he took his place in the reception room, but it may have been apparent to some that he was not entirely at his ease. He undoubtedly had knowledge of what Law would propose and, studying the harsh and gloomy faces around him, he wondered what reception the proposals would meet.

As Law entered the Palais Royal, he felt the tension at once. He sensed the antagonism back of the silence in the anterooms. But he was aware also of something else; the ministers of state might frown and fume but the people as a whole were with him, heart and soul. He was certain that the royal attendant who led him back through the crowded chambers was saying something like this to himself: "M'sieur Las, M'sieur Las, make me rich too. Give me just one little tip. Even the poor desire to be rich and I, M'sieur Las, I am very poor."

Law stated his proposal concisely but forcefully. What he asked was that his company should be allowed to take over the Farmers General which collected the taxes of the kingdom. For this he would pay an advance rent of three and a half million livres yearly. This would be the last step to absolute control. If the Regent yielded the right to collect taxes, he would make John Law more powerful than any minister who had ever wielded control in the shadow of a throne.

It is probable that the mind of the Regent had been made up in advance. France had already been transformed. Factories were humming once more, artisans were back at their benches, the shutters had been taken down from the windows of stores, the peasants were again able to sell their produce at reasonable prices. All this John Law had done. The Regent was undoubtedly ready in his mind, therefore, to take the final step.

The decision did not take long. In less than an hour John Law was in his handsome carriage once more, making his way back through the streets of Paris. His brother was silent, as if bewildered by the astonishing success scored.

"How much will you wager, brother William, that in less than a week our Company will assume the collection of all other branches of the king's revenues?" asked John Law.

"I know better than to gamble with you!" replied his brother.

In three days' time, John Law had reached the peak of success—he was the financial king of France, with more power than any other man in the kingdom. Within a few months he was appointed the Comptroller-General! Now there was left only the molding of his new empire in Louisiana and the beginning of the flow of wealth from its shores.

FOUR

The French Grow Rich

1

IT WAS LIKE WATCHING A BUBBLE GROW AT THE END
of a child's pipe. It grew and grew, getting so large and
round that it seemed certain to drift off into space at any

moment. And each moment it took on more wonderful colorings. Every shade in the rainbow was there, every brilliant combination known to nature.

Already people were beginning to speak of Law's operations as the Mississippi Bubble.

It was proving a great success. Prosperity had come back to France because people had more money. The money was made of paper but it was being accepted. People could go into a shop and buy what they wanted with it. The shopkeeper was ready to accept their paper notes because he could use them in turn. Perhaps, however, it would be better to say it seemed to be proving a great success. M'sieur Las said the prosperity would last forever. But who could tell?

Everybody in France wanted to get rich as quickly as possible, just as M'sieur Las told them they could. People wanted to own shares in his company so that there would be no doubt about this. They were already spending the money in their imaginations. The first shares of M'sieur Las's Mississippi Company were gobbled up immediately. For 500 livres a man could own a share. The more he talked about what he was going to do with his profit in the great company, the more his neighbor wanted to own a share.

In May, 1719, twenty-five million smaller shares were put on the market. This wonderful chance to get rich made the people money mad. A few months later M'sieur Las had to put over a *billion* of these shares on the market. Even the cobbler and the lantern-bearer began to scheme how they could become stockholders in the Mississippi Company.

People grew more and more excited. And M'sieur Las was very clever. He promised that twice a year those who owned the new shares would be paid very good interest. There was a rule, however, that no one could buy this new stock unless he or she owned some of the shares which Law had already put on the market. Now people started rushing around buying and selling the shares in his company. This was just what M'sieur Las wanted. In twenty days these billion and a half new shares were all snatched up and the lists were closed.

Never in the history of the world had there been anything like this. France had gone money mad. The few voices raised in caution were drowned. This was what is known as a "bull" market. As the people bought and sold, the price of the shares went sky high. It was a proof to all the people in France who saw themselves becoming as rich as lords that John Law had been right.

It was not only a boom in stocks. Everything was going up. There was a sudden demand for land and the prices of real estate went up and up two or three times. Food became expensive. In June bread had sold for three sous. By December it was costing four to five sous. But what of that? Man used bread only to sop up the gravy of his roast of mutton or the fine crisp capon which graced his table.

The world was watching France with avid eyes and visitors came pouring in to see the miracle with their own eyes. It was established that 25,000 foreigners came to Paris between October and December of this year of skyrocketing prosperity.

2

On the right bank of the Seine River in Paris, there was a certain street that felt the magic of John Law in the most amazing way. It was called the Rue Quincampoix, and it was a narrow, malodorous thoroughfare scarcely more than an alley. At one point it was not more than twelve feet wide and in length it was only fifty yards or so.

In ordinary times it was just like dozens of other winding gutter-filled side streets of Paris. Street porters and tradespeople tramped to and fro crying out about their wares. The ear had to be very sharp to catch their words in all the hubbub that was so typical of the streets of Paris.

"Bellows to mend—buckets to mend! Hot baked potatoes! Fresh herring—fresh water here!"

Their voices drifted up and echoed against the dirty façades of the houses, but the people of Quincampoix who gazed out of windows decorated with flowerpots and bird cages were so used to this racket that they scarcely heard it. They were accustomed, too, to moments of excitement in Quincampoix when a mad dog sent people scurrying, or the wind brought down one of the numerous iron signs suspended over the street, or a fat man slipped in the filth of the gutter and was helped to his feet by at least half a dozen *gamins* who hoped to get one small *sou* by way of reward.

But the new Quincampoix Street really bewildered them! Now it was jammed from one end to the other, from the first ray of dawn well into the night. It seemed as if everybody in Paris was turning into the Rue Quincampoix determined to be one of the pressing, sweating, shouting mob. The voices had a new unfamiliar cry, and they gathered in volume until there seemed to be a constant roar—*Mississippi! Mississippi!—who wants Mississippi!*

Gazing down from their windows, the amazed inhabitants of Quincampoix could see dukes and great ladies, bishops and butchers, farmers, pale-faced clerks and every conceivable type of person, all turned stock jobbers anxious to buy or sell shares of M'sieur Las's fabulous venture. For Quincampoix had become the stock market for the Mississippi Company.

Of course everybody wanted to be rich, so everybody flocked to Quincampoix. Now the district of Jaque de la Boucherie was the financial center of Paris. The great concourse of the Rue St. Honoré which ran eastward and passed the magnificent buildings of the Palais Royal and the Place du Palais Royal had to take second place.

It was merely en route to Rue Quincampoix where a fortune could be made overnight. Even the glamor of the Place Dauphine, where the gaming houses and cabarets attracted the pleasure-loving and adventurous, were forgotten in the wild excitement that gripped the little street with its few humble bankers' offices and homes.

On the days that shares were to be issued by the Mississippi Company, hordes of people jammed into the Company's offices on the Rue Vivienne. The lucky purchasers then made a mad dash for Quincampoix. Trading was done in the open street and it was just like a stock exchange, without the order and regulations of such a business center. In addition to the trading of Mississippi shares, big real-estate deals went on in the midst of all the bedlam. Noblemen's castles, laborers' cottages, farms, factories, country estates changed hands again and again as people struggled to raise enough money to share in the boom.

The crowd was so great that two heavy chains were placed at each end of the street in an effort to control the traffic of fortune hunters. The gentlemen entered from a street called Aubry-le-Boucher while the common people had a separate entrance by way of the Rue des Ours. In the mob of traders and curious bystanders no one but the powerful porters of the King's brokers could make any speed through the crowd, and their method of sharp thrusts of the elbow and knee brought a howl from those who were in their way. To the shouts and general clamor of business were added frequent oaths and shrieks of angry and frenzied men and women, all bent on becoming rich.

"Our Rue Quincampoix is a madhouse!" wailed the residents. However, after the first shock they were quick to see that they were living in a gold mine. The value of their homes and offices soared like kites in a brisk west wind. Homes that had rented for 800 livres a year now brought 5,000 livres a month. Every inch of every building from cellar to garret was quickly turned into quarters for traders and brokers, and those shrewd enough grabbed at concessions for eating places on the street.

The cobbler of Quincampoix, a quiet fellow who worked in nothing more than a shed made of rough planks against a building, quickly transformed his humble corner into an office. His work bench became a desk,

Fortune hunters jammed into Rue Quincampoix.

a few chairs were installed for the ladies. It cost him very little to get ink and paper, and before he knew it he was rich beyond all his dreams.

The hunchback of Quincampoix became wealthy, too. Being small and wiry, he had a way of squirming under elbows and appearing just at the moment someone needed a desk.

"A stroke of the pen may be your fortune, kind sir. My back will do as well as any table of oak. You'll do well to use it, sir!"

In no time at all his back had made him a fortune, substituting for a desk.

People were so greedy and desperate to become shareholders in the Mississippi Company—one share placed them in the ranks of the wealthy!—that Quincampoix was haunted all through the night. It was impossible for the residents to get any sleep. All day long they listened to excited voices rising to a screaming pitch. Voices were still clamoring in the murky light of the torches long after they had gone to bed. They tossed and turned and groaned and wished for a few hours of sound sleep in spite of all their wealth.

Finally, the law took over and an evening horn was blasted above the confusion and shouts of the mob. This was the signal that trading was over for the day. Even so the perspiring, delirious crowd was loath to go home. It took the police to push and herd the motley crowd of fortune seekers, brokers, swindlers, pickpockets and the curious out of Quincampoix, clearing it until the morning hour when eight drums beat out the signal for trading to start once more.

In this noisy crowded street scenes of human drama were taking place all day long. Men suddenly found themselves rich beyond their dreams. A coachman who had never even held a gold coin in his hand sold his Mississippi shares at such a profit that he was able to rush off and buy the biggest, most extravagant coach in Paris. His neighbor, a poor lantern maker who staggered around like a drunk—he was so overcome by his riches —found himself eating his pigs' feet and onions served on solid gold plate such as a nobleman would have on his table.

No wonder Quincampoix was the scene of delirious excitement and joy. "Why should we work when we can become rich?" asked tradesmen and artisans. So they put up their shutters and hurried off to join the crowd. Carriages all over France, even wagons spread with straw, were booked to take eager buyers to Paris. Meanwhile, work in the towns and villages had to wait and the harvest lay in the fields forgotten.

The spirit of gambling seemed to roll over the whole of France like an immense wave. Those who could not take part in the big gamble of John Law's Company dreamed up all kinds of ways to make extra money. People wagered on the number of Paris-bound coaches that would be hurrying through their villages on the way to the big scene of money-making. Men gambled on getting high fees for the use of their vehicles, and won. It was said there was scarcely a carriage in the whole of Paris that was not taken over for Rue Quincampoix. And every gaming house in Paris was busy day and night.

No one could keep a mind on business. Even the doctors found their patients' troubles a burden and had little time to attend to them. There was the greedy doctor from the Halles district of Paris who grumbled and fumed because he had to leave Quincampoix to visit an ailing woman.

"Ah me, it's falling, falling!" he muttered as he held his fingers on her pulse. Immediately the good lady shrieked and swooned, believing herself to be as good as dead. She, poor soul, did not know that her doctor was groaning about his bad luck on Quincampoix Street.

Just as some made fortunes, there were many who lost them. Greedy noblemen sold estates that had been in their families for centuries in order to share in John Law's easy, fantastic way of geting rich without working. Husbands and wives became estranged, and brothers quarreled violently. The poor were able to gorge themselves with food, and the rich found themselves faced with hunger.

The magic of Quincampoix had turned France upside down!

Whenever John Law appeared there the crowd became even more frenzied and clamorous. Of course his handsome carriage, one of the most elaborate in Paris, was permitted to pull into the adjacent street of the even narrower Rue Venise. This was a signal for the pushing, eager stock jobbers and buyers to shout out his name and press as close as possible to him in the hope of getting a tip on the market.

3

What was it that John Law's Company proposed to do? It promised to make so much money out of the country along the Mississippi that people who owned shares would become rich. It was as simple as that. People rushed in to buy these shares which kept getting more and more costly with each day, each hour, each minute. What did it matter how high the price was! The wealth of this fabulous land of Louisiana would make every shareholder rich.

The boom in the stock of the Mississippi Company started at once. Beginning at a valuation of 500 livres, the shares began quickly to climb. By July, 1719, they had doubled. By September they had reached the fabulous figure of 5,000 livres a share. Two months later they had doubled again, to 10,000 a share. Would this never end? During the winter months the climb was maintained and shares were being sold at 15,000 livres.

Amazing things were beginning to happen to all the people who had the shares. Some of them were sharp speculators, some were sound businessmen, most of them were rather stupid people who had stumbled into the market by accident. A servant had been sent by his master to that fabulous center of financial wizardry, the Rue Quincampoix, to sell 250 shares at 8,000 livres a share. Why the master entrusted such an errand to a servant is not known. He must have been either a very trusting fellow or a very stupid one. Strange things were happening in Paris, people were going mad. Well, trust the servant he did: and so behold the good Grimaud coming to Quincampoix and having no difficulty at all in selling the shares. He sold them not for the stipulated 8,000 livres but for 10,000 a share, and in cash moreover! Grimaud, honest fellow, put the money his master would expect safely away in a wallet. The rest he considered his own and began to speculate with it. In a few days he was a millionaire.

One of the favorite anecdotes of this period of colossal folly was that of a man who bought a few shares with a bit of money which had come into his possession. Well satisfied with himself for the daring and discernment he was displaying, the new investor went into a restaurant and, with a lordly disdain for prices, ordered himself a roast capon and a bottle of the best Beaujolais wine. He feasted royally. His enthusiasm was very considerably dampened when he received his bill and found that he owed 200 livres! A fortune squandered on a chicken and a small bottle of wine. What would his wife say about this!

He had to empty his pockets to pay the bill and he emerged on the street a wiser man. Here astonishing news awaited him. While he had been plying his knife and fork, the magic of M'sieur Las had been operating at an accelerated pace. The shares he had bought for himself had gone up in value, away up.

"Better sell," said the dealer who had handled the purchase for him. "There is already a nice profit."

The man thought of the cost of his dinner, of the disapproval he might expect at home.

"Very well, M'sieur," he said to the dealer. "We will sell."

The shares were sold and to his amazement the lucky speculator found that the magic of M'sieur Las had made a rich man of him while he stuffed himself with capon and drank his half bottle of wine. He had made a profit of 40,000 livres!

A valet made fifty million profit, a bootblack forty, a waiter thirty. The word "millionaire" had been exclusively English up to this time but now the French imported it, made it their own, smacked their lips over it, loved it. And why not? In France very soon every man would be a millionaire. The blessings of God and all the saints on that good John Law!

The most spectacular of winners was a widow of Namur named Madame Chaumont. She was not a wealthy widow. On the contrary, she depended for her living, poor woman, on some money held for her by a man in Paris. She went to Paris to collect her principal, a little apprehensive that she was not going to find things as they should be. This was in 1718 and all she knew of John Law and his schemes were things she had heard her friends and relatives say. What she had heard of him had frightened her. It may have been, in fact, that she had decided to claim her money because of the wild schemes of this daring foreigner. Ah, if she could only get her money and take it back safely to that dear Namur! It was furthest from her thoughts that she would find herself involved in the maddest financial upsurge since money had been invented.

Her apprehension proved well founded. There was a furtive look in the eye of her debtor which she did not like. He hemmed and hawed. He was hardly in a position, he said, to—well, to pay her the full amount of the debt. Would she accept it in state paper? The widow was not very bright but she knew that state bonds were down in value. Her estate had been small enough to begin with and she could not afford to have it cut to pieces in this way. The debtor was sorry, in fact he was quite desolated; but it came down to this, she must take his offer or have nothing at all. The widow, having no alternative, accepted shares in the Mississippi Company.

She took her shares back with her to Namur, believing herself ruined. The shares were probably worthless and certainly they did not pay dividends. Her friends shook their heads when they heard what had happened. Their poor old friend had been "taken." She might well heat her home with these worthless sheets of paper; but how was she going to keep a home? Her relatives tore their hair in rage. This old head of cabbage had thrown everything away, they said, and now they would have to support her.

Then rumors began to penetrate as far as Namur. This man Law was accomplishing miracles after all. One

day a friend of the widow, who happened to be a notary
and had a shrewd head for figures, paid the widow a
visit.

"How many of those shares do you have, my dear
old friend?"

The widow told him.

"Would you care to dispose of them?"

But the widow had been hearing the stories too. "No,"
she said. "The shares I shall keep."

He told her then that they were worth 15,000 livres.
This was a fortune, it was comparative wealth! Madame
Chaumont gasped with incredulity and then delight.

"You must sell now," said the lawyer, sternly. "Get
your profit before they go down again."

But the widow, who was not as stupid as they had all
thought, said, "No." She did not intend to sell. Not yet,
at least.

The debtor in Paris wrote to say that he had been
having some unexpected good luck. He was now able to
pay her the full amount he had owed her. He would
send the money on to her if she would return those
worthless shares to him. Madame Chaumont did not

The widow Chaumont refused to sell her holdings.

bother to reply. When the notary came by, as he often did, to ask if she wanted to sell now, she always answered with a shake of the head.

When the boom reached its peak, the widow Chaumont sold her shares and realized sixty million francs for them. She bought a chateau in the country and lived there like a dowager duchess. Friends and relatives flocked around her. The table she maintained was quite fabulous. Always there was the best of everything, particularly of wines—the lightest of champagne, the full-bodied burgundies, the fine white wines from the country of the Gironde.

Madame Chaumont was an outstanding example but there were tens of thousands of other humble people who did well in this mad "bull" market. There was no excuse any more for poverty since that fantastic man, that wonderful M'sieur Las, had waved his magic wand over France. The meek were indeed blessed, for they were beginning to inherit the earth.

Of course John Law was able to help many of his friends at Court to become fabulously rich. One of these was the Duke of Bourbon, the son of Louis XIV and Madame de Montespan. The Duke was often present along with John Law at the lavish parties given by the Regent, and he was often seen at the opera in the royal box. This was not because he held a position of wealth, however, for his family fortune was broken by enormous debts.

The Duke of Bourbon was good company. He was a close friend of the Scotsman's and among the first to receive a tip on the Mississippi Company, or the Company of the West as it was later called. Naturally he was quick to take advantage of it, and what happened to this impoverished nobleman is almost incredible.

In no time at all he had liquidated his debts and rebuilt his castle at Chantilly. Now he had so much money that he could buy large tracts of land between the Oise and the Somme, and a beautiful estate in Picardy which he had always coveted. Like most people he had several dreams of what he would do with a fortune. Some of these were extravagant dreams, but with 60,000,000 livres in his hands he was able to make them come true.

For many years he had longed to possess really fine stables and the best breed of race horses. He wanted to improve France's breed of racers so he imported one hundred and fifty of the finest racing breed from England. The new stables in which they were carefully tended were the finest in all of France.

The Duke had another dream—one of collecting zoological specimens and creating a center at one of his estates that would be open to the public. Now there was no reason why this should not come true. Money was flowing freely from his hands. The festival that he gave in honor of his daughter cost more than a hundred families in Paris would have to pay for food in a year— yet he scarcely dipped into his fortune to pay for it.

Of course John Law's chief sponsor, the Duke of Orleans, was among the most successful in the trading of Mississippi stock. He was as generous as he was extravagant with his soaring riches. He gave thousands of livres in gifts and pensions. The son of his friend the Prince of Conti was given 60,000 livres and the Count de la Marche another 100,000 livres. He gave lavishly to charities—one million to Hôtel-Dieu Hospital General and another million to the Foundlings' Hospital. Nor were the prisoners of Paris forgotten. Their debts, amounting to one and a half million livres, were discharged through the lavish good will of this acting monarch.

And what of John Law who made this great flow of wealth possible? He too had amassed a great fortune. But unlike his brother William, who invested his money in England and other countries outside of France, no doubt anticipating the day when he would return home, John Law invested his money in real estate in the land of his adoption. Fourteen estates now belonged to him throughout France. The Marquisat d'Effiat cost him 800,000 livres. He now had a title—the Marquis of Rosny. He possessed not only one castle, but many.

John Law was rich in friends, too. Princes and peers haunted him. Lady Catherine Law found herself followed by ladies of the court wherever she went. A hundred carriages bearing the most distinguished personages in France could be seen pressing toward the courtyard of Law's home when he was holding a levee. John Law was besieged by everyone. To have a word with him was the ambition of thousands of Frenchmen. To receive a smile and a gracious nod from the Comptroller-General was recognition coveted by the members of the Court and the lowly people of France.

Honors came to this financial genius from his native Edinburgh. The key to this great city was sent to him in a gold box, with great ceremony. The freedom of the city was extended to the Right Honorable John Law whom they had once rejected.

This was magic indeed—from wastrel youth who squandered his family inheritance, to wandering gambler in Europe, to the financial wizard of a great new France. But the man who supplied the magic was sincere. He was genuine about his interest in his new country. He put 8,000,000 livres of his fortune into France herself, investing in land and buildings. This son of Edinburgh truly believed that France would become the world's leading nation.

4

But now John Law had a problem to solve, the hardest problem he had ever faced. The ultimate prosperity of his Mississippi Company depended on his ability to make it pay dividends—fat, juicy dividends. Louisiana was virgin territory, a great stretch of empty land where a few tribes of Indians and many herds of buffalo roamed. It was not going to be enough for him to make France rich in anticipation of the miracles which would come about when the land west of the mighty Mississippi had been settled. Did John Law have visions of great industrial cities and huge stretches of land covered with waving corn? Perhaps, but that was of the distant future. In the meantime he must see that the country was settled and the natural resources tapped. He must be an empire builder as well as a financial wizard and promoter.

So he took the problem to the Regent and received authorization from that most accommodating of men for everything he was going to need—ships, guns, supplies, artisans, farmers, men, women—for a miracle of colonization.

But the bringing to pass of this miracle was going to depend on another man. Law knew that the French hold on the mouth of the Mississippi, which was the key to the settlement and the wealth of the West, depended on a patient little band of French-Canadians under the command of a man named Jean-Baptiste le Moyne, Sieur de Bienville. This man must be set to work.

He saw to it that a sheaf of orders was sent to Bienville. He must select a site for the capital of the projected new state and build a city there at once. There was not a day to be lost, not an hour. The ships would be on their way before these orders reached him— in fact, a whole fleet of ships filled with sailors and soldiers and supplies and loaded to the gunwales with food. There would be horses and cattle and sheep and agricultural tools. Most important of all there would be hundreds of settlers and hundreds of handsome plump women—king's girls, they were called—to marry the settlers.

FIVE

Bienville, the Real Hero

1

IT WOULD MAKE A BETTER STORY IF IT COULD BE SAID
that Bienville knew nothing of what was happening
in France and that the instructions sent to him were

in the nature of a bombshell. The truth of the matter is that he had received reports of the strange excitement which had gripped all of France, and he had anticipated some such move as this.

The news that he had been appointed governor was, however, an offset to the startling order that he must create a city in a matter of weeks. He was being accorded an honor which should have been his many years before. It had been withheld for reasons he had never understood and now he began to form his plans with a right good will. He had no illusions as to the outcome. His superiors in France expected miracles; and Bienville knew that miracles are not easy when they must be wrought with a handful of men and a few tools, and the primeval forest as a background.

There was never any doubt in his mind as to where the much needed capital city was to be located. That wide, slow bend of the river, which he had seen with his brother when they first ascended the Mississippi, was the ideal spot. It was there he would make ready for the influx of settlers, the men and women who were to wring wealth from this aloof land.

He moved men and equipment across the Gulf at

once. To save time some of the men went through the arm of water which is now Lake Borgne and completed the trip to the bend by land. Most of the boats went farther south to the mouth of the river and then battled their way up.

It is refreshing to leave France behind, in telling the story of how Louisiana came to be settled and the West to be opened up. It raises the spirits to turn from the wild and selfish orgies of speculation in France to the little group of French-Canadians who, year after year, held the mouth of the Mississippi against all opposition. John Law, the great gambler and financier, has always occupied the center of the stage. For once he is going to be accorded his proper role. Law was the villain of the piece, and Jean-Baptiste le Moyne, Sieur de Bienville, the real hero.

The arduous nature of Bienville's work has already been shown. Far harder for him to bear, however, had been the mental strain under which he had labored. While he held the fort in Louisiana, his valiant brothers had been dying. Now only four of them were left: Charles, the oldest, Joseph de Serigny, who was with the French navy, Bienville himself, and Antoine, the youngest of the ten, who was serving with him.

It was fortunate that Charles still survived because he had taken over the leadership of the family on the death of old M'sieur Charles, the father. He was as brave as any of the younger sons but his role had been to build up the resources of the family and supply the funds for the adventurous exploits of the others. Charles had made a great fortune in the fur trade (in which all the brothers shared), had been made a baron by the king, and had converted the family estate at Longueuil into the grandest chateau in America. Later he would act as lieutenant-governor of the country and would be killed in the wars with the English.

It is probable that Bienville had felt a particularly deep grief over the death of the fourth brother, Paul de Maricourt. Little is known about the characteristics of any of the brothers, but one thing recorded of Paul gives him a reality that some of the others lack. He was smaller in stature than the rest and the possessor of a great gift for negotiation. He had a way with Indians and always acted as the family ambassador. Even the Iroquois liked him and called him

Taouistaouisse, which meant Little-Bird-Always-In-Motion. His death from the hardships of a campaign against the Six Nations Indians two years before the catastrophic end of Iberville had been a sore blow to all the surviving brothers.

Perhaps the thinning of the ranks stirred Bienville to even greater efforts. It remained for him to keep the flag flying, to carry on one pair of slender shoulders the burden which ten had once borne. Certainly he proceeded to perform wonders in his efforts to change the swamps of Louisiana into the El Dorado which Law had promised the people of France.

It is probable that the site on the Mississippi looked less favorable to Bienville now than on that eventful day when he and his brother Iberville saw it for the first time. The end of the Indian portage was a litter of discarded canoes, of old weapons and useless cooking utensils. The ashes of countless fires had turned the soil to dull gray. Everywhere else the trees grew down thick to the river banks. Rain had been falling and now a dank mist rose from the water. Bienville looked about him with a discouraged eye. "Here," he said to himself, "I must build for the Regent a city which will bear his name forever."

He lost no time in speculation or regrets. The end of the Indian portage was partially cleared. This, then, he would make the *Place d'Armes*, the center of civic life and activities. The busy axes soon had the space cleared completely and, in accordance with his plan, Bienville built two barracks on the sides for the accommodation of the troops. The north side of the square he was reserving for the cathedral, and all he could do now was to erect a shrine and stretch canvas across it. At the southwest corner, he raised a frame building of one story which was to provide administrative offices. A far cry, this, from the city of his imagination, which would be a cluster of stone buildings in the shade of pine trees—a city of high spires and slate roofs and carved balconies.

Bienville had with him an engineer named Pauger and the latter proceeded to clear the land, using a squad of convicts for the work. He then cut streets through the scrub trees and underbrush. The blocks fronting the river opened out from the *Place d'Armes* and the government powder magazines were located on Dumaine. The house planned for the Intendant was to be between St. Peter and Dumaine Streets, and the headquarters of the Company of the Mississippi were on the block above. Bienville, who now had the title of Governor, intended to erect for his own use a house of no particular size on a square one block away from the governmental buildings.

This was the plan. Needless to state, all the buildings designed did not spring into existence at once. The sites intended for them had been only partly cleared and no effort had been made to get out the stumps. The chief necessity was for log huts and tents which would provide accommodation for the flood of settlers John Law was sending over.

A miracle had been expected of Bienville. He had brought it to pass; in a partial degree, at least. But he was not satisfied. "What will they think, these poor deluded people, when they see this?" he asked himself. One of his chief difficulties, he knew, would be keeping peace among the settlers when they discovered what Louisiana was like.

The first to arrive was a small party of eager and hopeful people under the command of a M. Dubuisson. He had been given a large grant of land and had organized his own party, made up mostly of his own family, his brothers and sisters, and twenty-five employees.

"Where is New Orleans?" was the first question Dubuisson asked when he stepped ashore and gazed first at the squalid conditions and the rude buildings of the *Place d'Armes,* and then at the trails leading back into the cover of trees.

"Here, M'sieur," answered Bienville. "This, you must understand, is no more than a beginning."

A feminine voice cried out loudly from the landing place where the newcomers had seated themselves on the piled-up boxes and luggage. "But we read all about it in the *Mercure.* The new city with eight hundred beautiful houses!"

"M'sieur le Gouverneur," said Dubuisson, in a voice which showed he already realized the extent of the disaster in which he and his people were involved, "they showed us the plans of the city. Was it, then, nothing but a hoax?"

"As to what is said and done in France, I do not know," answered the Governor. "All I know is that

"Where is New Orleans?" demanded the newcomer.

this is a rich and wonderful country and that some day it will yield great wealth to us. But, M'sieur, it is going to take time, much time."

It was some moments before Dubuisson spoke again. "They were so helpful," he said; "they were even explicit. They told us all about raising silkworms and tobacco and the growing of cotton. They showed us reports."

"This country calls for patience and courage," said the Governor. "I have been drawing on my share for many years. But I think I still have enough left. I trust you have plenty of your own, M'sieur."

2

It becomes necessary at this point to look back at France to see what John Law was doing to secure settlers for the new empire and the inducements he was citing to raise such great expectations in their minds.

He had discovered something about the Frenchman that he had not known before. The true son of France had no desire to leave his Paris, or Amiens, or his little village nestled among the tall poplars. He did not want to go across the ocean to a strange land to become a "Mississippian." It was far better to stay home and by any means, whether it meant selling the farm or the family inheritance of a castle, to become a stockholder in the Mississippi Company and get rich at once.

But John Law had not been stumped for long. He had devised a remedy that seemed exactly the right tonic for the home-loving Frenchman. As he sat at his desk, shut away in his inner office at the Royal Bank, there lay before him, spread out, dozens of tracts. These were the labors of his journalists. They, too, had dipped into a bag of tricks and had come up with a delirium of words that was to infect the whole nation.

William Law, studying these along with his brother, was dismayed at the extravagance of the word pictures of the Mississippi. "No one will believe this writer, John. He says that the soil has merely to be scratched with a minimum of labor and lo! a crop springs into being, only to be followed by one, two, three equally abundant harvests throughout the year."

"And this one,"—he picked up another leaflet— "that even the most humble home dines on venison, woodcock and pheasant." His voice grew more and more incredulous. "Is it possible that the Indians do worship the white man, that they wait on him like a god, so that no Frenchman going to the Mississippi will have to lift a finger unless he wants to?"

John Law looked up with a smile. "I'm willing to gamble on others asking that question and going to the Mississippi to find out!" he said.

William Law read on, frowning to himself, his look of amazement growing. Louisiana was a Paradise on earth, according to the tract writer, who then went on to prove it in glowing words. A picture was given of a land decked with "carpets of flowers" and with an unending season of spring, with "air like wine" and "heavy with the scent of magnolias." The flowers and the vegetables in France were like midget growth in comparison. There was enough fish in the rivers, lakes and streams to feed a whole nation. Indians were pictured as strong, God-fearing braves and the maidens more desirable and beautiful than all other women.

John Law did not listen to his skeptical brother; he was fingering a soft curl that flowed down his shoulder from his lavish wig. "Our plan about bringing over the Daughter of the Sun, the young Indian princess, was an excellent one. I couldn't have planned it better. The government has come up with the idea that it might help our cause if she were to marry a Frenchman. Yes, a beautiful young Indian woman to a Frenchman. What do you think of it?"

"I happen to have heard the rest of the story," replied his brother wearily. "She refuses to marry except in the tradition of her family. This means she has the right to get rid of him *by death* should he turn out to be, shall we say, not satisfactory!" He gave a short laugh. "Huh! I doubt if she will find a husband among the French. They are too fond of living!"

But John Law closed his eyes and his mind traveled in imagination to the shores of the great River, to the broad stretch of water that young Bienville was always writing about, proclaiming it to be the only site for *New Orleans,* the capital of Louisiana. There, for a moment, he saw himself in the Paradise so ably described by his writers, in a veritable palace—Mississippi style, of course—and no less impressive than his castle-like Marquisate of Rosny, and a fitting domain for the emperor of Louisiana.

Suddenly he sat up, alert, smiling in a pleasant re-strained way as he was likely to do when the odds were in his favor, when fortune was smiling at him. "Yes, that's it! I shall create duchies and mar-quisates. The rich will fight to get in on *this*. I my-self will become a grantee. It is quite possible," here he became the confident gambler who so carefully planned his next move, "that I shall form societies, headed by authentic noblemen!" He began to choose them, counting them off on his fingers. "These great leaders among our peers and society will send out de-pendents under the supervision of an intendant. I my-self will send hundreds!" He spoke convincingly as if his plan were already in full swing and a success.

His brother paced up and down the office, making no comment.

"Louisiana has been a drain, William," said John Law, with a trace of sharpness in his voice. "We can-not allow this to continue. Louisiana is our credit. It must be our profit. Without people, it can't be!" He stood up and gathered the tracts in a single pile. "We know from experience that there is only one way to success: find a need and fill it. We need emigrants.

People must be induced to go!" He held the tracts up. "Look *beyond* these words, William. Look beyond!"

The set look on his brother's face relaxed for the moment; it was not hard to be won over by the easy persuasive manner of the other man. Then he sighed. "I feel as if all France has gone crazy, John, from coachmen to bishops. Two hundred livres annually, interest on every five hundred livres' worth of stock—no wonder everybody wants to own just one share and be classed among the wealthy. And look at the way it soars —fifteen, twenty times its value and still higher . . ."

John Law picked up his hat and tucked it under his arm. One glance in the mirror assured him that his gay, extravagant clothes were in order, his wig in place. "Come! We'll see if it is as dangerous in Quincampoix as it was yesterday. Another man was crushed to death in the crowd. We must try and prevent this sort of thing."

William Law followed his brother and took his seat beside him in the heavy, garish carriage with its rich red velvet and gold fringe. He was weary and greatly disturbed. A visit to Rue Quincampoix was always like part of an absurd dream to him, a nightmare in which the street and its occupants were stripped of reality, leaving him bewildered and uncertain of his reason.

As usual a crowd had formed and many were running alongside the carriage, trying to keep up with the pace of the horses.

"It is getting impossible to be alone," sighed John Law. "Not even in one's own bedroom! Would you believe it, dear brother, a woman was so anxious for a tip about our Company that she tried to climb down my chimney. And last night," he chuckled as he recalled the scene, "a very beautiful duchess had her coachman upset the carriage right in front of my house. I fear I failed the dear lady. I could not bear to leave my dessert at the moment, so I sent my servants to her rescue. Though my own coachman has recently become a capitalist, my present footman was unable to give her any advice about *Mississippi!*"

Another thought came to his mind but he decided not to share it with his brother. He had lingered over that same sweet at his dinner table while a number of people awaited him in his antechamber. It had given him one of the greatest satisfactions of his life, for among those who were obliged to await his pleasure

The duchess had her coachman upset the carriage.

was none other than a member of the Royal family—
the Prince of Conti!

3

Such were the inducements which filled the minds
of the people who landed off the flatboats used by the
resourceful Bienville to bring them up the river. Was
it any wonder that they exploded in wrath and threat-
ened to burn the squalid little settlement and compel
the crews to take them back at once to France?

Bienville realized the enormity of the deceptions being practised on these unfortunate people. Being a faithful servant of the state, however, he proceeded to carry
out the orders he received and to improvise measures
to meet the emergencies which arose. The situation
became more desperate with each new shipload.

It was apparent to Bienville almost from the first
that the right kind of people were not being recruited
by the flamboyant methods of John Law. They were
not the settler type, the hard workers who would plant
crops and build houses for themselves and gradually
make the country independent of food supplies from

103

France. Instead they were fortune seekers who had been attracted to the new world by the promise of easy ways to become rich. When they found there were no streets on which gold could be picked up, that there were no spice trees, that the natives were cruel and treacherous, that, in fact, Louisiana was no more than a trackless wilderness, they reacted as might have been expected. They gave up and sat themselves down in anger and despair.

Among the newcomers were troublemakers who stirred up dissatisfaction and crooks who separated the more gullible of the settlers from such resources as they had. There were lawyers who preached sedition and found ready listeners.

Bienville did the best he could to maintain some degree of peace and at the same time he continued vigorously to push along his plans for New Orleans. His best, however, fell far short of satisfying the malcontents. The letters they sent home were filled with complaints of him. In course of time this clamor of discontent reached the ears of the Regent and he concluded that Bienville was to blame. He decided to send out a new governor.

It was John Law who saved Bienville. The former went to the Regent and expressed his conviction that Jean-Baptiste le Moyne was doing as well as any human being could under the circumstances.

"His reports show him to be a hard worker," declared Law. "He's a sound man. I would gamble on *that*. He knows the country. He believes in it. Instead of getting rid of him, give him more help."

This was decided upon. As a first step, capable engineers were sent out to aid in building up the town and opening the land along the rivers and bayous.

This was an important turning point in the history of the colony.

SIX

The Bubble Expands

I

MEANWHILE, THE SUN WAS SHINING UPON A WILDLY
excited France. The whole country had become a nation of swindlers and money-intoxicated people. Life,

especially in Paris, was like an endless festival. The magic scraps of paper of the Mississippi Company had put gold into the hands of rich and poor and now it flowed out as easily and lavishly as it had poured in. People were as eager to spend their money as they were to make it. No one had time to notice that the Mississippi Bubble had expanded dangerously close to the bursting point.

There were so many fabulous things the new-rich could now purchase. Art treasure such as France had not seen in many years began to flow into the country. Now not only the great ladies and gentlemen of the Court wore silks and satins, but cooks and parlormaids as well, who were present at the Opera in the same fashionable apparel as their former mistresses.

Rare jewels decked the hands of women who had known only drudgery before the spell of John Law came over France. The humble folk were able to buy new small round wigs, while the much-powdered wig of the nobleman was styled to be larger than ever. The waistcoat was cut to a dashing low design and there was scarcely a gentleman who did not wear a gold-embroidered coat. My lady's patch-box was decorated

107

with real pearl and, of course, she chose a different patch with every new and frequent change of costume. There was the so-called *gallant* patch placed in the middle of her cheek, or the *passionate*, the intriguing beauty spot by the corner of her eye to attract the glance of other eyes.

An intoxicating gaiety had captured the streets of Paris. Strolling musicians and little groups of entertainers, acrobats and jugglers now roamed not only the lively Place Dauphine but also other promenades made fashionable by crowds of pleasure-seekers.

No one had time for work. No one had thought of anything but the Mississippi and that glorious empire of Louisiana across the ocean which was going to pour even more gold into France.

The gossip about the Regent's parties filled the people with delight, although there had been a time when his extravagance had horrified and angered them. And even the widow Chaumont was discussed in Paris because her table was said to groan daily with an ox, two calves, six sheep and numerous fowls, prepared by the best chefs in France for her hordes of guests.

Naturally the baker's son who spent 400,000 livres

to buy gold plate for his table felt a kindred spirit in the Regent and wealthy noblemen. His fingers itched to get his hands on more money. Like thousands of others, he wanted to own land in Louisiana even though it was selling at 30,000 livres a square league. He had no way of knowing that most of this land selling at twenty thousand dollars a square league in the money of today was merely wilderness frequented by red men.

Shares in the Mississippi Company were now selling at thirty-six times their value. The bubble was at the bursting point. But the people went gaily on, thinking of luxuries, dreaming of more wealth, bent on pleasure, quite unmindful of the future.

The glory and wealth that John Law had predicted and promised for France were fulfilled. The name of this Scotsman who had saved their country and made them rich was shouted in a roar of approval that echoed over France. Only a cautious minority of the people was aware that the ever-expanding bubble was trembling precariously.

2

Thousands of tracts with John Law's fabulous stories of Louisiana and the Mississippi River found their way into every corner of France as freely as scattered leaves on an autumn day.

There were pictures of Indian maidens with large soulful eyes, gazing upon their new masters. Gallant braves knelt before the French colonist. Even in the little villages of France, the people were familiar with the town plan of New Orleans and well informed about the health-giving qualities of this new land across the ocean. The peasants were thoroughly instructed on the subject of their benefits as emigrants. The most extravagant words pictured their new homes, the land they were to receive, the finest of livestock that would roam their pastures.

The adventurer was given every promise of finding gold and silver lying in huge lumps ready to be seized and turned into riches. Gold dust was said to gather in the streams as thick as the sand of Louisiana.

The women of France who might be interested in matrimony were intrigued to learn that hundreds of

Louisiana Indians performed in a Paris theatre.

yearning Frenchmen and French-Canadians were waiting for them on the shores of the Mississippi. All they had to do was to pack their belongings and M'sieur John Law would see to it that they sailed off to Paradise.

At first there was an onrush of enthusiastic men and women and youths with a longing for excitement. Carts jammed full of these new emigrants could be seen rattling through the streets of Paris bound for the ports. The vehicles and the horses were decorated with fluttering yellow ribbons. Those Louisiana-bound wept and laughed and shouted their farewells. The aged sighed and wished that they too could be young again and go along with them. Even the home-loving Frenchman was bewitched for the moment and caught up in this spell, wondering if he too should not grasp the chance to make himself a fortune in this wonderful new world of the Mississippi.

The most amazing things were taking place in Paris. Men with reddish-brown skins and dark eyes, strange shaven heads with single forelocks of hair decorated with feathers, were to be seen in the streets of Paris. They performed on street corners, wrestling to show

112

off their mighty strength, attacking each other in mock battles with weapons strange to the French.

These natives of France's new empire appeared at the Italian Theatre along with the most famous performers. The audience gasped to see their feats of strength and cunning. Never before had they seen such weird dances as when the Indians donned their feathers and paint and stamped about the stage. The unfamiliar beat of the Indian drum rang in their ears for the first time.

Other strange sights met their eyes. The Cathedral of Notre Dame was crowded by people curious to see the baptism of a young Indian girl, very pretty and intelligent-looking in spite of the strangeness of her native costume. The Bois de Boulogne was the setting for something the French people had never seen before —a stag hunt staged by the Indians from Louisiana, just as if they were galloping through the trees and brush of their own native forests. How they could ride, and what strange sounds echoed through the woods as they shouted in true Indian fashion! These young Indian braves were magnificent, said the Frenchmen. What a glorious new empire we have across the sea,

113

they told each other. But actually, after the first rush of emigrants, few people wanted to leave France and go there!

3

As the bubble grew bigger and bigger, John Law's problems increased. According to the charter of his Company, he was required to send six thousand people to Louisiana within a period of years. Thanks to his genius in publicity he had managed to get shiploads off; but he wanted not hundreds of emigrants but thousands! His Mississippi stock was climbing dizzily. The interest going out to the stockholders was a tremendous drain. He had to have a profit from Louisiana! This was impossible without emigrants.

At first he tried to get colonists from various sources such as prisons and orphanages. These he knew would not make the best citizens for Louisiana but he was desperate to carry out his plan.

Once again he resorted to publicity to try and stir up interest among the Frenchmen.

One morning in Paris, those who were passing the

prison of St. Martin des Champs stopped to peer in the prison gates curiously. In the fresh morning sunshine stood two rows of prisoners, one hundred and eighty men and the same number of women.

"What is happening here?" asked a passing watchmaker who was staring through the bars of the gate along with other curious people.

"A mass execution, I'll wager," said one gloomy man. "The price of food is soaring. It's costly to keep criminals!"

But the faces of the prisoners were not those of men and women about to die. Some had an expectant look and even dared to whisper in spite of the roars of the guards. Others who had been led from solitary confinement blinked in the sun and were dazed. There was a restrained air of excitement throughout the courtyard.

Then, to the amazement of the passers-by, a few orders were shouted and the two files closed in, turned and faced the prison, making a long queue of men and women paired off in couples.

Down the steps of the prison came the governor, his staff, and members of the clergy in their long black robes.

"Praise Heaven and the saints!" said the amazed watchmaker.

In a matter of a few minutes, these curious people at the prison gate had witnessed the marriage ceremony of prisoners bound for Louisiana. Then they were to witness another amazing spectacle. Guards rushed forward as the priest's words died away, as if there was not a minute to be wasted. Quickly the newlyweds were handcuffed together, each bride to her new bridegroom. With equal speed they were pushed into wagons that appeared at the opposite side of the courtyard as if by magic. The prison gates flung open and they rattled off through the streets of Paris, no longer prisoners but bound for France's new empire. John Law had no time to lose in finding workers for young Bienville on the Mississippi.

There were many other wagons full of prisoners bound for the seaports and ships ready to sail off to Louisiana. Thirty wagons of women prisoners rumbled through the streets of Paris. These were drunkards, knife-experts, the mentally subnormal and even women dangerously unbalanced. Such sights were becoming common and many people ceased to be curious and did not even take time to run to the windows or stop in the streets when the shout went up: "Mississippians! Mississippians are coming!"

However, had they followed the thirty wagons of female prisoners on the long ride to La Rochelle, they would have witnessed a sight not to be forgotten.

These women, when they learned their fate, refused to get out of the wagons when they reached the dock. There in the shadow of the great billowing sails they began to scream and kick and set up such a disturbance that every available man had to drop his work and run to the scene. It was fairly easy to dump the rebellious women out of the wagons, but once they were given elbow room and the firm feel of the docks under their feet, they began to fight. They used all the weapons of enraged women—tearing fingers, flailing arms, sharp teeth that bit into the flesh of the unfortunate guards and sailors who tried to force them up the ships' gangplanks.

Seamen and deckhands found themselves faced with a new peril in loading this human cargo. They felt sorry for the men in Louisiana who were waiting for these brides and would be marrying these wildcats in petticoats. It took the sharp explosion of muskets to bring any order, and when the hysteria died down, six of the women lay dead from the musket fire.

4

Law's journalists had painted a glorious picture of the voyage to France and Louisiana. Big, sturdy ships were described, well manned, they stated, with experienced crews, men who had crossed the ocean dozens of times successfully. The voyage, they wrote in flowing terms, could only be described as a dream voyage, with nothing to do but rest and stroll the decks, drinking in the bracing ocean air in anticipation of eating the ships' feastlike meals. These meals were prepared by expert chefs and were fit for the Regent himself; in fact, the trip to Louisiana was designed to please a king. Those who were Louisiana-bound would be waited on hand and foot and live like royalty.

With these promises in mind, the emigrants who boarded ship at Port-Louis and La Rochelle received a shock. There was a scene of bedlam at the docks. Last-minute repairs were being made to old and broken-down vessels. Sailors who had been "shanghaied" for the voyage spent more time fighting the crews than attending to their jobs. Ships' pursers struggled and fought to round up enough food for the weeks ahead, bribing and stealing in order to get at least a starvation diet for the passengers.

Ships were loaded far beyond their capacity both with supplies and passengers. Where were the roomy cabins the travelers had heard about, and the fine parlors and spacious decks? Their hearts sank as they were crowded down below in the holds where the provisions were stored or, even worse, along with the cattle bound for the Mississippi. In their alarm and bewilderment, they would have gone ashore at once and turned their backs on the voyage and Louisiana, but the ships' captains had been ordered to prevent passengers from changing their minds. Therefore reassurances were showered upon the troubled emigrants. Once they had set sail proper accommodation would be allotted to all passengers. The passengers on the previous voyage had sailed all the way to the Mississippi without complaint. The ships rode the Atlantic waves, even at their roughest, with the ease and smoothness of a stately swan on a pond. The poor travelers sank into the little corners of the airless and hot odorous holds, sick at heart, struggling to keep up their courage, hoping for the best.

Once the ships were out at sea, the captains and mates changed like chameleons. No longer were they reassuring and helpful. They had become tyrants. The de luxe cabin that a more fortunate and wealthy emigrant had paid for was crowded by three or four other passengers; and there was no arguing with the ship's master. When heavy seas brought seasickness to the ship's company, the more hardy of the men passengers were forced to do the work of the sailors, climbing up the riggings in terror and doing their trick of duty on the slippery wind-swept decks.

The sturdy chose to sleep up on deck when the weather permitted. As the voyage wore on and the air became more and more foul below, they slept on the deck through rain and windstorm, with nothing more than a bit of blanket or a basket to shelter them from the elements.

Many of the captains were inexperienced. Their ships floundered. Winds failed and ships were becalmed. The passengers died when old and young were stricken with disease. Even the scanty diet of moldy bread and cheese and a thick concoction more like glue than soup was cut down and down until the passengers were on starvation rations. It was far from a *dream* voyage for the new citizens of Louisiana.

5

Meanwhile John Law was combing France for more emigrants for his empire. The infamous Mississippi *bandouliers* appeared on the streets of Paris. These Bank Guards in their gray-and-blue uniforms and three-cornered hats were soon to be the terror of the streets.

John Law was still able to turn to his bag of tricks —this magician seemed never at a loss when he needed more power—and now he used justice as a means of getting what he wanted. New edicts were proclaimed that made it possible for his *bandouliers* to carry out their job of rounding up more emigrants for Louisiana.

Now anyone caught idling in the streets of Paris was breaking the law. A coachman taking a day off from his work dared not be seen loitering in the streets.

Passengers to Louisiana were forced to do hard labor.

The unsuspecting French boy from a village farm who walked the streets slowly, gazing about him, minding his own business, was snatched up by the *bandouliers* as a vagabond. The unemployed valet who did not obey the order to find a new position within four days of quitting his master was picked up as an idler. A beggar did not dare be seen by these men in the gray-and-blue uniforms for fear of being hurried off to a seaport and Louisiana.

These Mississippi bandits roamed the streets in great numbers. The people dreaded them. They were over-bearing in manner and frightening to look upon. Paris soon became divided into two camps—those who might be gathered up and sent abroad and so avoided the *bandouliers;* and those who saw in the police of John Law the hope of getting rid of some annoying or danger-ous person.

The *bandouliers* were only too glad to learn of a rea-son why a certain man or woman should be charged with lawbreaking. They acted quickly. There was never time for defense. They accepted bribes and were very successful in rounding up shiploads of new emigrants.

A few words and a few livres and an incorrigible

daughter was packed off to La Rochelle and the next ship due to sail westward. A jealous wife now knew how to get rid of a younger or more beautiful woman who had captured her husband's fancy. Husbands made good use of the *bandouliers* too, and an unwanted wife or troublesome female disappeared from the streets of Paris. Enemies contrived how to get rid of each other, with the amount of the bribes soaring sky high. One had only to sit down and write a short note to the police, expressing a suspicion. The *bandouliers* had a quota to fill.

A pall of fear began to fall over Paris. The people who gathered in the taprooms and cafés found more and more horrible stories from the Mississippi to exchange. As pedlars and street idlers disappeared from sight, never to be heard of again, the tradesmen and porters who had business in the streets were haunted by suspense. They made a great show of their business deals to prove that they were not loafing in the streets.

This murmur of fear grew into a rumble and finally demanded the magic touch of John Law. Frenchmen who never let serious problems spoil their pleasures over the gaming table or at the Café Procope now found their games disturbed as the rumors grew . . .

"Five *hundred* girls have been picked up in just a few days. Soon we shall have to go to the Mississippi to find brides for ourselves!"

Of course, as rumors will grow, this story had the whole city aghast. By the time it had circulated a dozen streets, every other child in three was being taken to the Mississippi and five thousand young girls had been spirited off!

With public opinion against the actions of the Bank Guards, John Law was forced to be content with the harvest of emigrants his men had reaped so far. Orders were issued that in the future the regular police was to accompany the guards. Each week a list had to be presented to the police of all those rounded up by the *bandouliers*.

Now people could sleep more easily without fear of being whisked away the next morning without being given a chance to cry out in protest. Everybody breathed a sigh of relief, especially the woman who had been nagging her husband, and the man who dreaded his rival. The traveling acrobat who performed in the streets of Paris now had a chance to plead his case when the *bandouliers* took him in charge. Now it was safe for a visiting peasant to wander along the Place Dauphine and mix with the street musicians, enjoying all the sparkle and excitement of a Paris promenade.

During the harvest of the *bandouliers* when dozens were arrested each day, the activities of the ports had mounted to a frenzy. Old and dilapidated merchant ships were hauled out of dry dock and fitted up the best way possible for the voyage. The blue flag with the white cross waved on the mast of many a ship that was a disgrace to the merchant fleet of France. John Law was sending colonists to his new empire but hundreds of them were destined to be lost at sea. Most of them were unfit for pioneer life. Those who were spirited away were bitter and desperate; many of them jumped into the sea, their minds cracking under the strain. The seas were churned by storm after storm and the poor little fleet of ships with its miserable frightened cargo suffered many losses.

Few of these new colonists had left France willingly. Not more than a handful cared about building a great new empire for their country. These latter were the people that young Bienville was counting on.

126

As the months passed by, the sorcerer Law had managed to carry out his dream, for nearly seven thousand five hundred colonists had been sent to Louisiana. But John Law's plan could hardly be called successful. One third of this number either perished or returned to France.

SEVEN

The Bubble Bursts

1

WHEN JOHN LAW WAS AT THE HEIGHT OF HIS POWER,
with all of France lauding him and bowing at his feet,
the magic that he had created got out of hand. He did
not need any crystal ball or augury to warn him that

the Mississippi Bubble was about to burst. For months he had been aware of the danger but at a loss to save his Company. It seemed the sorcerer had lost his magic touch.

The greed of the French people started John Law on the downward path from the dizzy heights of success. They now wanted to feel their money in their hands. Paper money no longer spelled magic to them. Those who had made huge fortunes overnight or within a matter of weeks wanted smooth gold to hoard away in safety. Suddenly they wanted proof that the Bank was protecting their fortunes with metallic money and not the paper money of John Law's *system*.

"The Prince of Conti has been taking his money out of France!"

Alarming stories such as this sped round the city. Not even John Law could prevent the people from knowing that millions of livres were flowing out of France, wagonloads of it, accompanied by hosts of well-armed men who had been seen crossing the borders.

"What dreadful omen is this?" the money-crazed people began to ask themselves.

The truth of it was that two thousand six hundred

million of livres were circulating around France in bank notes, while the bank held only thirteen hundred million of metallic money. Their paper money was close to worthless. The fear of the merchant and the housewife and the gay spender that the paper in their hands was of little value had become a reality.

John Law was a fighter as well as a gambler. Confidently, smilingly, though inwardly full of foreboding, he tried to cover up the true state of affairs in France. The person who needed a loan found that with proper security he could get his hands on money and pay only two percent interest. Within a very short time John Law passed thirty-six edicts in an effort to save his Company. People were forced by law to pay for their purchases, unless they cost very little, in paper money. Nor could they have metallic money hidden away under their mattresses or a loose board in the attic. The law obliged them to keep no more than five hundred livres in specie. The police searched houses for coins and unfortunate lawbreakers were dragged off to jail for treason.

Meanwhile, at Rue Quincampoix the people had begun to mistrust Law and his great ideas; they had lost faith in his Louisiana empire. Too many terrifying tales of life in this savage land had drifted back to France. Now people thought of the Mississippi with dread and thanked God they had not risked their lives in this wilderness. Many a candle was lighted for the souls of those who were at the mercy of the Indians and of starvation and disease; and tears were shed into the pillows of the rich and pallets of the poor for loved ones across the sea.

Mothers who were tired and impatient now had a new threat. When children became impossible, they said, "Hush! Hush—or I'll send you to the Mississippi!" The thought of such a horrible fate had the effect of a firm hand clamped over a howling mouth.

A wave of passion and foul play swept over the city. Eleven people were murdered within a few days in Paris. A man was robbed of his money and brutally cut to pieces on the Pont Neuf. The nobility of France suffered a great dishonor when the young Comte de Horn killed a wealthy Mississippian and paid with his life, his body broken on the wheel.

A cry went up against the narrow street where so many fortunes had been made. John Law, watching the reactions of the public closely, was quick to take action. All trading and selling were forbidden in Quincampoix, and plans were made for a new center for trading in Mississippi stocks. All the stock jobbers and brokers flocked into the Place Vendome. Hope of a quick fortune still had the poor and the rich in its spell.

The crowds in the Place Vendome were so dense that tents were erected. This was now the social center of Paris, the great concourse where *mesdames* were to be seen in their elegance, promenading, or seated at the little tables of the cafés or in the gay restaurants that had appeared miraculously. Gaming houses opened all around the district. There was no lack of entertainment for those who did not want to pursue business. Jewels and fabulous treasures were won with the turn of a wheel or the roll of dice. John Law paid millions of livres for the elaborate Hotel Soissons for his headquarters, and the gardens of the hotel were dotted with the jaunty touch of pavilions erected for the use of the brokers. It was all very gay and festive, part of his last desperate move to keep his Company's stock trading and the wheels of his enormous game still rolling.

Regardless of his clever manipulations and the false sense of excitement and gaiety that still prevailed in Paris, the people in France were growing to hate the man whom they had recently hailed. Overnight, it seemed, the lords and princes and the ministers of the government had deserted him and were now voicing their loathing; while the people in the streets grew bitter and spat at the mention of his name.

Over the din of church bells and shouts of the coster-mongers, the noise of rattling wagons and coaches, came the cry, *Down with John Law!* Little gangs of rebellious citizens gathered on street corners, growing in numbers until the police were faced with riots all over Paris.

2

Paris was gripped by fear. The people were desperate about their money. No one with a trunkful of paper bank notes could have traded it for a single gold piece. Gold! The people wanted gold and firm sound coins in their moneybags and in the Bank. A howl of hate rose from the throats that had shouted themselves hoarse with cries of "Long live M'sieur Las!" The new rich tossed and turned in their beds at night, sleepless, wondering if they had fortunes or enormous stacks of worthless paper.

John Law, still fighting to keep his head above the rising threat of ruin, had to resort to guards to get from his office to his carriage and through the streets to his home. Great mobs of people stood before his door, shouting insults, hurling rocks and shaking their fists at the heavily curtained windows.

John Law could not sleep at night. Memories of the days when he had been imprisoned in the Tower of London over the duel with Beau Wilson haunted him. He could hear the ominous sound of feet upon the stairs when the police came to re-arrest him. He broke out in waves of cold perspiration and his heart pounded at the thought that he might hear those footsteps again, stopping at his door.

The anger and hatred of the crowd had been turned upon his family and servants, too. Lady Catherine and the children had been pushed and insulted in the streets as they entered and left their carriage. There seemed only one wise course to take. They left Paris and took refuge in the country at St. Maur.

The Regent was another against whom many of the people of France turned, blaming him for his sponsorship of John Law. The Regent, though not openly deserting Law, was unable to help him beyond supplying the Scotsman with two companies of the Swiss Guards for his protection. He had to consider public opinion.

John Law felt very much alone in these dark hours.

3

One day a friend came to him with the most disturbing news. Parliament had made a proposal that John Law should be arrested by the vergers and taken to the Tribunal of La Tournelle.

"So—it has happened!" The Mississippi Bubble had burst, his life was in danger. With almost a sigh of relief, Law looked up from the shining black leather shoes with the red heels that marked him as a man of distinction at court. He waved his valet away and put on the shoes himself.

"You understand, M'sieur Las—the plan is to arrest you, try you and condemn you," said the friend.

"The execution will take place immediately. Should the king's troops come on your behalf, the gates will be closed. If they batter them down, it will be too late."

The eyes of the two men met.

"That is the plan, M'sieur Las," said the friend.

Without a word John Law stood up and continued his dressing. His face was expressionless, his manner composed.

"You must fly, immediately!" the friend advised.

On a crisp morning in December, 1720, while the gray dark of dawn hung over Paris, a post-chaise pulled away from the Palais Royal and turned into the Rue St. Honoré. The coach bore the arms of the Duc de Bourbon but the driver and footmen were dressed in somber and plain livery.

Through the darkness of the streets the misty lights of the lantern bearers could be seen. The weary wafer merchant lifted his doleful cry, hoping for a last sale or two. The brisk cries of the milkmaids rang out for the early risers who were waiting for milk. Paris was beginning to awaken and soon the streets would be full of carriages and wagons, horses and tradesmen crying their wares.

As the post-chaise made its way through the city and toward the open road, it was joined by a little group of horsemen, four equerries and six horse guards. With scarcely more than a few words to the occupants of the carriage the party proceeded along the road that led to Valenciennes.

A man and a boy sat close together in the coach. The boy was barely awake and his head nodded upon the shoulder of the man, lulled by the steady clip-clop of the horses' feet. The man was wide awake and staring down at his hands. He had shut his mind to the thought of what those hands had so recently held. Now his thoughts were upon the 800 *louis d'or* which he held and a few gleaming jewels.

Other than the few possessions in his luggage, the money and the jewels represented the fortune he was taking away from France.

"When are we going to see Mama and Mary Catherine?" asked the boy sleepily.

"In a very short while, my son," replied John Law. "They will follow us and we will be together again."

The carriage took John Law and his son into exile.

He smiled down at the boy who had so recently been honored at the games and parties of the boy king of France.

"Where will we go then?" asked the boy.

The ex-Comptroller-General of France did not answer. He was too concerned with the suspense of that hour. A few more miles and they would be safely across the border. His heart had been cold and thumping within his breast on one or two occasions but the little party had not been stopped; their flight had been uneventful.

The papers and passports in his pockets were signed with the scrawled handwriting of the boy king. The Regent had vouched for the safety of his life as he fled Paris in a borrowed post-chaise, under armed guard and in disguise as Monsieur de Jardin.

Yet John Law felt an oppressive sense of foreboding as the post-chaise rattled on toward Valenciennes. The strain of the weeks had played upon him physically; his body ached and his mind, usually so quick, seemed heavy and clouded. He could think of only one thing, safety from the seething, shouting mob in Paris that wanted his life.

A light fall of snow had drifted over the coach windows and John Law peered through the frosted pattern to gaze upon a country village. Church bells were ringing and the joyful spirit of Christmas seemed to have pitched the voices of the children into delighted shrieks as they ran after the post-chaise, their dogs at their heels.

One of the equerries drew up his horse beside the coach and lifted his hand in a gesture. Only two more miles and they would be safely across the border. John Law sighed with relief. He lay back against the cushions and closed his eyes.

He was dozing when the equerry next spoke to him, opening the door and letting in a frosty gust of wind. "We have arrived, M'sieur. I will present your papers."

The boy slept on. John Law tried to relax once more against the soft yielding cushions but some inner tension gripped him. In a few minutes the equerry returned and asked him to step into the Intendant's office.

With a sinking heart, John Law climbed out of the carriage. The eyes of the equerry avoided his. The man's face was strained.

John Law stepped into the lighted office and looked

into the face of the man behind the shining oak desk.
The Intendant was Monsieur d'Argenson, son of one
of his greatest enemies, the ex-keeper of the seals.

D'Argenson had a wicked gleam in his eye. He was
very polite. His words were few, his voice smooth and
slightly tinged with irony. It was too bad but M'sieur
Las would have to be detained. He knew that the former
Comptroller-General was anxious to get on his way for
his winter vacation in Brussels but there were certain
reasons why his plans would have to be changed.

John Law did not attempt to argue. His white face
showed little expression. Silently he returned to the
carriage and gathered the sleeping boy into his arms.

The next forty-eight hours were agony for John
Law. The Intendant made no explanation as to the
delay. John Law would not give him the satisfaction
of pleading for permission to continue.

Toward the end of the second day, the sound of a
galloping horse could be heard as a rider swung into
the courtyard.

It was a messenger from the Regent. He brought
with him a peremptory order to let M'sieur Las and
party proceed.

Again the party started out. Soon the border of France was crossed. Once more John Law was an exile.

For a number of years John Law and his family moved from place to place throughout Europe. Never again did he return to France. His fortune and his property had been confiscated by the government. He was a poor man now. His host of friends had dwindled down to a few only. His travels finally took him to Italy where at one time he had made a fortune at the gaming table. He still gambled with what little money he had. He was still full of great ideas of how nations could make money and prosper. But no one listened to him now. He had gambled with a nation's resources and lost.

He was living in Venice when he died in his fifty-eighth year. He was buried there, quietly, with few to pay him their respects.

EIGHT

After the Crash

1

THE MISSISSIPPI BUBBLE HAD BURST. THE MAN WHO
had been responsible for it, who had been called so
fervently the saviour of France at the start and then

universally criticized as a thief, had fled the country. For every millionaire he had created, he had made a thousand paupers. Unemployment had returned, bringing with it two invariable companions, want and class hatred.

The government took sharp measures to meet the situation. It is almost certain that the Regent, that well-intentioned roué and amateur chemist, had little to do with the housecleaning. He was sitting in the ashes of humiliation like a Job who had brought about his own misfortunes, too frightened and shocked to initiate any steps. The Pâris brothers were recalled to take financial matters in hand. The interest rate was then further reduced to revive confidence among businessmen. Law's Bank was abolished and the creak of its hinges as the doors closed was the final proof that the System of the wizard had failed. The Mississippi Company was whittled down to a small trading concern.

One of the first measures of the Pâris brothers was to take a pool of the wealth of France. It seems to have been done thoroughly. It succeeded, certainly, in finding where the profits of the madness had gone. It was discovered that more than a hundred individuals had amassed fortunes of twenty million livres or more and that most of them were still in possession of their gains. Countless people had benefited in lesser degree. All over France people were trying to conceal their assets.

It was decided to make the winners disgorge and this was accomplished by fines, so large that they amounted almost to confiscation. The largest winners were assessed as high as ninety percent. No effort was made, however, to touch the winnings of the nobility, for France had not yet learned that a ruling class had responsibilities as well as privileges. The Duc de Bourbon was said to have been the biggest winner in all France but his gains were not touched. The Prince of Conti took three wagonloads of money out of France and no guard raised a hand to stop him at the border. The Regent himself had profited enormously but it is not on record that he gave any of it up.

Among those who were caught in the pincers was that hearty winner, the widow Chaumont. Either she had discovered a latent shrewdness in herself or she had been shielded in the final stages by the wings of luck. At any rate she was reputed to be worth sixty million francs when the Bubble burst. The government agents demanded that she pay back eight millions of it. The widow did so without protest. She could live out her life in comfort on what was left and have more than a chicken in the pot every day!

It has already been made clear that the man at the bottom of all this excitement left France without diamonds hidden in the heels of his shoes or hoards of gold in the lining of the carriage. He left with practically nothing. Lady Catherine Law remained behind in Paris, at great personal risk, until debts owing to tradespeople to the amount of ten thousand livres could be paid.

The money taken out of the pockets of the winners was not distributed among the losers. The shrill clamor of a million claimants would have filled the air if this had been attempted. It would have taken years to decide between the honest claims and the spurious. The money, after the costs of collection had been paid—and it may be assumed that they were heavy—went into the government coffers where it was needed. As is always the case in the history of great booms, the winners kept very little and the losers had nothing but empty pockets.

NINE

New Orleans

I

THE BURSTING OF MONSIEUR LAS'S BUBBLE PRODUCED
another problem for France—Louisiana! Several thousand Frenchmen and their families had sailed across
the Atlantic believing that they were going to a para-

dise of riches. Those hardy men and women who survived and who were still there were thankful if they found enough to eat, let alone riches. What was France going to do about these people?

The little colony was tough, fortunately. All the hardships and bloodshed and disappointments had brought forth some results. Chemists and soldiers and adventurous clerks had turned pioneer, beginning an empire on the river banks, on the plains and in the thick of the forest. So far they had won out, even with the great odds against them.

Naturally the government in France did not want to admit it had failed by bringing all the people back. It was decided the experiment across the seas should continue.

Shortly after the festival of the Moon of the Buffaloes in December, ships of the French merchant navy approached Biloxi with their red-and-white flags flying in the breeze. The ships' holds were jammed with supplies and provisions. New emigrants were crowded into every available corner. These passengers were bringing news, news that was to amaze Louisiana: Las's *Bubble* had burst!

On board were two hundred Germans who knew how to work the land and raise fine crops. John Law had sent them out, a last desperate effort to make Louisiana start paying its way. There were also a hundred men for the land grant of the Marquis d'Anceny. Seventy trained and reliable men were on board for Monsieur Kolly. A far-seeing Jew, Elias Stultheus, arrived with a number of hand-picked settlers, a million dollars' worth of merchandise, and the first wheeled vehicle to touch the shores of Louisiana—a lumbering wheel chair.

To add to the confusion the Company had sent along a shipment of six hundred Negroes to serve as slaves.

It was Bienville's job to allot all these emigrants to new homes and plantations. Of course he had never given up the hope of making New Orleans the capital of the colony. This had been his ambition as a youth. Now that he was reaching middle age he refused to give up the idea. He was persistent and determined. Scarcely a ship headed toward France that did not have a letter or a report from Bienville urging that New Orleans be the center of the colony.

There were men around him who had other ideas. Monsieur Hubert, the king's commissary, had land in the Natchez country and he wanted to see a capital built there. The agents of the company, the crafty L'Archambault Villardo and Legas, were pulling hard to have it located at the Gulf where they had plans that would make them very rich. Naturally all the merchants and traders in the Gulf settlements did not want the capital to be moved to that crescent moon-shaped spot on the river. For many years it was doubtful whether Bienville's and his dead brother Iberville's ambition—and that of La Salle, for he had dreamed of a city on the Mississippi!—would ever come true.

When the Bubble burst, New Orleans was far from being a capital settlement and certainly not the city of beautiful homes, of spice gardens and high spires that Law had pictured. It was no more than a cluster of grim little shacks.

For several years after Bienville got orders to start a settlement there and went out with a party of fifty men to clear the land, it was barely more than a trading post. But finally the day did come when the first citizens of New Orleans were to begin in earnest to build a city. And these men built like experts. Their "crescent city" was to be no hit-and-miss job. They

151

planned and constructed so well that it was to stand firmly and little altered through the years into the next century. Its original typical flavor and plan can be seen in the New Orleans of today.

These men who knew little about road building and carpentry rolled up their sleeves and took orders from De Pauger, the engineer. The plan for New Orleans was the work of De la Tour; he patterned it after Rochelle in France. It was on a parallelogram plan and this was divided into squares. Each square had a drainage ditch around it—not to beautify the landscape, by any means, but to fight Ol' Man River when the yellow waters boiled over its banks. Houses were built within these squares; they were roughly made out of split cypress, and roofed with bark. Usually they were only one-story high and mounted on piers or blocks. In the early days they were surrounded by willows and pools of water swarming with insects and reptiles.

These men toiled under the broiling sun, planning for the days when the fashionable ladies of New Orleans would roll along the streets in their carriages. The streets were fifty feet wide and perfectly in line. When they were named in 1724, it must have made many a colonist homesick—St. Anne, Condé, Royal Bourbon, Toulouse, St. Louis. The French influence was to be carried on by those American-born Frenchmen and women who were later known as Creole. Many of these street names are to be found in New Orleans today.

The blocks fronting the river were set aside for the market place and the military. The cathedral that young Bienville had imagined towering above the city was to have a place of honor on the square. The homes of the first citizens were clustered around the market and parade ground on the river front. Houses soon spread out toward the Bayou St. Jean.

Today the traffic on this waterway is made up of sailing craft out for pleasure. In those days this picturesque placid bayou was an important thoroughfare. The first residents of the bayou saw a steady procession of emigrants pass by their doors, crowding the boats that took them to their new homes.

Many of these people were so new to Louisiana that they were dazed by all the strange sights of the new colony, or wracked with fears about living among savages. This bayou country was gentle enough—people still love to wander along by the water there—but it was strange to them with its moss-covered oaks and cypresses with slimy trunks and weird vines that made a jungle of the growth. More than one woman traveler shrieked at the sight of an alligator sunning itself in the gentle current. It was here that an Indian girl who had been bought as a slave is said to have grabbed an axe and saved the life of her master, the historian Le Page du Pratz, when he was cornered by a giant alligator.

Four years after the land was cleared and the first rude huts put up, word came from the Company of the West to move the colony to New Orleans. This was a red-letter day for Bienville. He had been arguing that vessels could sail up the river from the mouth through safe channels. He had even proved it in the exciting adventure of passing over sand bars safely with vessels. Now, in the month of June, De la Tour and De Pauger started out with vessels well loaded, passed over the treacherous bars and sailed for New Orleans. Cautiously, other boats followed them. The people rushed to the docks to greet them. New Orleans was now a port. At last, in 1722, she was made the official capital of Louisiana. It had taken Bienville nearly a quarter of a century to bring this about.

This was only part of New Orleans' struggle. Everything seemed to be against her, making it hard for Bienville to succeed. In the flood seasons the water came up over the banks, with nothing to stop it. Buildings were swept away. In one flood the church, the hospital, and thirty houses were carried away. The citizens had to flee for their lives.

Monsieur Mathurin Dreux was considered a lucky man. He is said to have been with Bienville when he actually began the settlement at New Orleans. He directed the clearing of the land and was given the reward of a valuable grant of land. The section he chose was richly wooded, running over a ridge and continuing like a rampart behind New Orleans, high land away from the danger of the floods. Part of this is Metairie Ridge today, the truck farmers' section; part belongs to Gentilly Terrace, a lovely suburb of New Orleans.

While some settlers had to build and rebuild their homes, Monsieur Dreux was never at the mercy of the

155

Mississippi. He was able to work without this threat, making bricks, raising cattle, clearing the lands for pasture. He had many slaves, and he and his brother Pierre were in time able to build a beautiful house with large rooms and galleries. This house was surrounded by fine gardens and for a century it was the showplace, the pride of New Orleans. Descendants of this early settler are still well known in Louisiana.

2

Floods were more often than not followed by famine and sickness. One year a deathly fever carried off two people a day in New Orleans. Bienville was taken ill and for days the people waited anxiously in the square, hoping to hear encouraging word from Monsieur le Docteur.

But the fever was not to put a stop to Bienville's work. While the colony was growing up, the English, the Spanish and the Indians had to be fought off. The savages worked swiftly and cunningly. They struck in the land of the Natchez, or in the east from the

Carolinas where the English planned to edge into Louisiana, exciting the Indians of that region against the French. They struck westward on the Gulf, where the Spanish were well established.

When word came to Bienville that France was at war with Spain, he decided to take Pensacola. Many years before, his brother Iberville had urged France to bargain with the Spaniards for this settlement. Bienville started out by land, with soldiers and savages. His brother Joseph de Serigny had come over with soldiers from France, and with four ships laid siege to Pensacola from the Gulf. A warning had been sent to Mobile to have a party ready to join Bienville.

As they moved in on Pensacola, the Spaniards gave up without a fight. Three hundred Frenchmen were left there to hold the fort and the Indian braves were sent home. The troops marched back to Mobile. Immediately the Spanish swooped down and recaptured their fort. This spurred them on to an attack on the Isle of Dauphine, a threat to the French colony at Mobile, but the troops of Louisiana had once more mustered and the Spaniards were beaten off. In retaliation the

French struck out for Pensacola again and stormed the fort. There were nine bilanders and two captured French vessels in a fight that was short and violent. In an hour's time the French had captured the whole lot. A fleet of five ships from France had arrived just in time to join in the battle.

The Indian warriors who had attacked with the French were given a reward. They were allowed to plunder the fort and carry off what they could. Before the day was over both forts were completely sacked and burned.

3

A hurricane did its best to break up the settlement at New Orleans during one tropical storm. It smashed down the crops, and the famine that followed was the worst the settlers had ever known. Many times the Indians had saved the lives of the colonists with supplies of food from their own stocks. Now they were starving too. Then came a plague and this carried off many.

One day one of the directors of the company issued orders that anyone who wanted to return to France could do so. The struggling colony was thrown into hysteria. Feverishly they began to pack and make plans to get away on the first ship to France. No one could think of anything but escape from this terrible, savage land.

Excitement mounted and it seemed that no one would be left in the whole of New Orleans. Bienville had to make a desperate move. He cancelled the permission. Three ships, the *Dromedaire, Loire* and *Deux Frères,* were ready to sail, their sails hoisted. Bienville had to call out troops to keep the cursing, weeping men and women and bewildered children from fighting their way on board.

When this panic ended, the colonists settled down. They rolled up their sleeves once more and rebuilt damaged homes and warehouses. With fine weather and good crops, they accepted the life in Louisiana and made the best of it. They were even getting used to the mosquitoes and snakes.

Some excellent men, many from the best class of

French peasants, had come out to work on the land grants. They brought plows from France. If anyone could make things grow they could. They took great pride in producing bigger and better fruit and vegetables than could be found in France.

Sawmills and brick kilns were built and plantations cleared along the river. Tobacco factories kept new emigrants busy for long hours of the day. Then there was a Monsieur Hubert who made himself very rich. He brought out a miller and several millstones from France and built a water mill. People brought their grain to be ground, and his concession in the Natchez country was one of the finest. He had also brought over a gunsmith and an edge-tool maker so he built a forge mill on the river that served the colonists for many miles around him. A neighbor of his, Monsieur de Montplaisir, put his thirty tobacco workers out on the land, and in the second year they produced more than thirty thousand pounds of tobacco.

Life was full of excitement and uncertainty for these new citizens. Bienville had to send an armed brigantine to take Monsieur de la Harpe's family and party up the river. Word had come to him from faithful Indians that unfriendly savages were not going to let the Frenchmen build a fort near their home on the Rivière de la Madelaine.

Sure enough, about twenty leagues up the river, armed savages came swooping out from an ambush on both sides of the river. De la Harpe and his Indian guide shouted out to them that they came as friends. The Indians refused to listen. Frightened women and children wanted to turn around and go home—home to France, away from the hideous savages and lonely river country. Finally nine of the warriors were coaxed on board the brigantine. They agreed to go to Biloxi and talk it over with Bienville. The party relaxed. Bienville was known among the Indians as a man whose words could be believed. He had rarely failed to make peaceful terms with hostile tribes.

Far up the river in the country of the Arkansas, several hundred German people had settled. They had come out to work Law's concession in this country. When they arrived at Biloxi their troubles began. First of all they starved on the hot sands of the port. They saw hundreds of Negro slaves, slowly dying from neglect and starvation, dumped at the port of arrival more like unwanted stores than human beings.

The land that the Germans were given was covered with huge pine trees. It took a whole day to cut some of the biggest timber down by axe. They had to clear the land of masses of pines and thick bush that was bound up in twisting vines. There were savages ready to leap out upon them from this jungle. Snakes and alligators were underfoot. Bears and wildcats tracked them down; panthers sprang out of the trees upon them. They had to fight the river in the spring. Yet they did not give up. They built little white houses and worked from dawn to dark. Many of them died from hardships but those who survived made wonderful colonists.

When the ships arrived with news of John Law's flight from France, there were more Germans on board. The first who had come over clamored to go home when they heard that Law's reign was over. Bienville persuaded them to stay. He could not afford to lose such fine workers. He offered them new fertile land on both sides of the river twenty miles above New Orleans.

Once more land had to be cleared and homes built, but it was not long before there were rows of neat little houses surrounded by gardens. This settlement was called Côtes des Allemands and it is still known by this name.

More than once the fruits and vegetables of these hard-working Germans saved the colony from hunger. There were times when ships from France failed to come with provisions for the colony. Then the sight of the little boats of the Germans loaded with produce, coming down the river, would bring every man and woman to the docks to welcome them gratefully.

These Germans were known as such hard workers that in later years when the Creoles spoke of work that was unusually hard they said, "It takes German people to do that!"

4

During these hard times New Orleans was gradually growing into a real capital settlement. A party of fifty miners would come with one ship; another would bring

163

five hundred barrels of flour. Within four years' time more than twelve hundred women were sent out by the Company. Some of these were French girls who would make good wives for the colonists.

In 1721 there was great excitement in New Orleans. Word came that the ship *La Baleine* had anchored at a roadstead on the Gulf with a prize passenger list— eighty-eight girls who came out under the care of a nun from the Hôpital Général de la Salpêtrière. These were orphans cared for by the Church, and each one came with her *dot*. They had been sent on this great adventure with skirts and petticoats and bodices and bonnets, like brides; and they became brides, very quickly!

Many of the men of New Orleans had been followers of Bienville for twenty years. Now they stood behind him staunchly, as ambitious as he was to build a great city. By 1726, New Orleans had grown so that a census was taken. There were more than eight hundred people belonging to those first families of New Orleans, including two hundred or so slaves and servants.

The streets had taken on definite character. The finest was called Bienville. This was where the governor's house stood, and that of the Surgeon Major of the hospital. The hospital stood on the Rue de Quay, which is the Old Levee Street of today. Near by, Monsieur Pauger had built himself a house.

A man could take his musket to be repaired to the cannonier who had his shop on St. Philippe Street. Carpenters, shoemakers, the wagon maker, and even a man who would make wigs to order, were grouped together on Royal Street.

Back of the houses stood the servants' quarters and the kitchens, also the little offices where the help got their orders for running the household. The flowers that grew in the gardens came from seeds and cuttings brought over from France and Havana. Tall, pointed picket fences surrounded the houses just as they did in France.

Deep ditches surrounded the houses, protecting them from the flooding waters. These squares were like islands; that is how the word "islet," still used in speaking of a square in New Orleans today, was first used by the colonists.

Things were pretty rough in those days. Women who were accustomed to beautiful homes in France found themselves in rude cabins. But they insisted on having

165

servants and using the fine crystal and silver brought over from France. They wore fine silks and high-heeled slippers and danced the minuet. They brought satins from France, and brocades and snuff boxes. When there was plenty of food they had the very best on their tables, even swan and venison and pheasant. At first they rebelled against bread made of flour mixed with corn or rice, not wanting the corn bread of Louisiana; and it took them some time to get used to eating hominy, which was cooked with grease and included pieces of fish or meat. They had their *café au lait,* of course, for the Frenchman loves his coffee made with hot milk. They had pineapples and watermelons and bananas and pecans; and other new foods such as sagamity and sabotins, a kind of eggplant.

Nine years after that spot on the curve of the river was cleared for the site of New Orleans there was a curious mixture of people there—rough ex-soldiers and criminals, trappers, miners and fortune hunters. But there were many others as well. Their families became the "first families" of Louisiana. Later on, a hundred years later, their descendants formed a class of society that included many fine Creole families.

François Philippe de Marigny brought the name of De Mandeville to Louisiana. He was the commander of Fort Condé near Mobile. His name stands first among those of the old Creole families in Louisiana. Another connected with New Orleans is that of Jean Joseph Delfau de Pontalba, who came in 1732 when New Orleans was still struggling to survive new hardships.

The family of Villere can be traced back to a man who came from Canada. He was with Iberville and the first expedition. He lived on land belonging to Bienville. Near him lived the Chauvin brothers who became noted for their prosperous plantation. Other well-known Louisiana families are connected with De la Chaise, who came out as a commissioner for the Company of the Indies in 1722, and De LaFrenière. Descendants of a man named De Kernion still live in New Orleans today. Others can trace their family history back to Jacques Esnould de Livaudais, who was given the post of pilot of the Port of New Orleans after sailing back and forth across the Atlantic on ships that brought out hundreds of emigrants.

5

In the days that followed Law's flight, the colony in Louisiana had more than floods and Indians and France's enemies to fight against. There was still a Mississippi Company and the directors were determined to make money. They began to issue orders. These did not surprise the French-Canadians working with Bienville—they knew how the government worked!

The people of Louisiana woke up one morning to find that they had to buy their supplies from company stores. A proclamation had been issued to that effect. What was more, the prices were fixed. No ships other than those of the Company were allowed to stop at Louisiana ports for trade. The settlers had to pay high prices for supplies but they got little for their produce in return.

French-Canadians had lived through a hundred years of this kind of treatment. Had the Company said to the people, *Work for yourselves and for Louisiana, raise your tobacco, sweet potatoes, beans and rice; make yourselves rich on your plantations and in the forests trapping animals!* people would have flocked to

Louisiana. There was wealth in the colony even if not the kind of riches Monsieur Las had pictured.

But the story was quite different. The Company was interested only in making the people work for its good. It took the Creoles of Louisiana years and years to bring about the most important thing—an order of life that was built on freedom and peace. Because of these people it was a life of charm and gracious living—something quite different and beyond compare.

Bienville never stopped working and fighting and planning for Louisiana. Yet there came the day when he was recalled to France. So many charges had been made against him by jealous men that he was called home to give an account of himself. The French and the French-Canadians had not worked together well. They bickered and were jealous of each other.

Bienville was accused of favoring the Canadians. For twenty-four years he had been the man who faced each new crisis. The good of Louisiana always came first, yet he was to be dismissed with a pension of three thousand livres. This was his only reward for a lifetime of service. Not one of the officials who had worked under him was kept in office. They were all discharged in disgrace.

Perier, who took over from Bienville, tried to bring about some good in the colony. He built levees to protect New Orleans from the floods. These extended eighteen miles up and down the river from the capital. But he did not know how to deal with the Indians.

One day, five years after Bienville left Louisiana, Fort Rosalie, which he had built to protect the country of the Natchez, was suddenly attacked by hordes of Indian warriors. The fort was soon taken and only a few people lived to bring news of the tragedy. They had a terrible story to tell. The Natchez had wiped out the whole garrison.

The people of New Orleans were in a panic. All work was forgotten. The market place and parade ground were crowded with anxious citizens. They were sure that the Natchez would strike at New Orleans next. Every man was needed to help build a palisade around the settlement. Every boy and girl big enough to carry a pail of water or basket of food for the workers was kept busy. Under the broiling sun, trees had to be cut down and barricades built.

170

Jean-Baptiste le Moyne, Sieur de Bienville

In this time of suspense and danger, the people of New Orleans longed to have Bienville as their leader. He had led them against the Natchez Indians in two wars in 1716 and 1722. Hundreds of men had lost their lives but the savages had been subdued, and Bienville had brought about a treaty with them. The people did not have the same confidence in their new governor. They wanted Bienville, believing him to be the only man who could save them and the colony from further attacks.

The palisade was hurriedly raised and armed men stood guard day and night until the suspense lessened and the danger was over. Nevertheless, the terrible fate of Fort Rosalie was not forgotten. The people sent an urgent request for France to send Bienville back to them.

One day a ship sailed into the roadstead bearing an important and honored passenger—the first royal governor of Louisiana. It was Bienville. The company of the Indies had given up its charter and now Louisiana was in the hands of the state. New Orleans and all of Louisiana welcomed him back, believing that he was the only man who could lead them successfully.

6

This was to be the brave French-Canadian's last appearance in the role of leader. His health was not good and the years were piling up on his shoulders. He came willingly, nevertheless, for this was the land he loved—this land of canebrakes and deep forests where the air was scented by the wild fruit and the eye was ravished by the bloom of the magnolia. He was willing to expend all the energy he had left in the effort to save Louisiana. He was willing even to die in that cause.

Bienville led the French troops against the Indians; he fought strenuously to bring the Natchez and the Chickasaws to account. He attacked again and again, and he tried to bring about terms of peace. Finally in 1742, weary and discouraged, he asked France to let him retire. This request was granted, and the day came when one of the ships that set sail across the green waters of the Gulf for France took Jean-Baptiste le Moyne away from Louisiana for the last time.

TEN

Louisiana Is Given Away

1

BIENVILLE NEVER WENT BACK TO CANADA. NO DOUBT
he was influenced by the fact that all of his valiant
brothers were now dead with the exception of Antoine,

the youngest. The streets of Montreal would have seemed cold and bare, and the chateau at Longueuil a sad place, without one of the ten to greet him.

After his final recall, he took a small two-storied house in the Montmartre section of Paris. His pension was not large but it was ample enough to allow him to live rather well. There were three male servants in the household, a valet, a cook and a coachman. The valet's name was Veuraine but for some reason his master preferred to call him Picard. The name of the coachman is not on record but to Bienville he was always the Baron, probably because he sat on the box with great dignity. The cook's name was Renaud. He seems to have been on a less familiar footing with the master of the house because no nickname was coined for him. It is clear, however, that an easy atmosphere was maintained in the little household and that the days and years went by easily and pleasantly.

Bienville enjoyed these final years. No longer exposed to the bitter cold of the St. Lawrence country or the stifling heat of the bayous, he was able to indulge in long walks. Necessity had imposed on him the most severe habits in the days of his governorship but now he could relax. There were no duties to drag him away from the cheerful warmth of the wood crackling in his small fireplace. Once condemned to the plainest of fare, he became a lover of good food and wines. He would discuss most earnestly with Renaud the dishes to be served each day.

They were pleasant days. It seemed that peace had come at last into the life of the man who had so bravely held the line of the Mississippi and that nothing could happen to disturb it.

2

When Bienville was eighty-four the king of France became weary of the responsibility and the cost of his colony in Louisiana. Perhaps the fact that Canada had been lost to the British weighed in this decision of the unstable king. Why hold so persistently to the mouth of the Mississippi when there was no longer any chance of making use of its strategic location? It did not matter that thousands of Frenchmen had died in finding and holding Louisiana. At any rate, the monarch let it be known that he was prepared to give the colony to

Spain. The shock of this disclosure was felt even more keenly by the old man in the little house on Montmartre than in the beautiful city which had grown on the site he had chosen. To think of relinquishing the mouth of the Mississippi, for which La Salle and Iberville had given their lives, was bad enough. But to hand it over to Spain, that closest of colonial rivals in the South, was unthinkable.

Bienville, slow of speech and step, went to Jean Milhet, the delegate from New Orleans, and poured out his grief and indignation. Milhet shared his feelings and they decided to demand an audience of the King.

Picard the valet gave a thorough brushing to the long-tailed blue coat. (It must have been blue because the men of Montreal always wore that color to distinguish them from the red-coated men of Quebec and the white-coated men of Three Rivers.) He took special care with his master's lace cuffs and saw to it that his tie was spotless.

But the King refused to see Bienville and Milhet. Louis XV was a casual monarch and it probably did not seem to him necessary to concern himself with a matter of such small moment. They were referred to the King's first minister, the Duc de Choiseul, and for reasons which were quite clear to both men this boded them no good.

The Duc de Choiseul had risen in the service through the favor of a certain beautiful lady whose name was Madame de Pompadour. He was a man of considerable ability nevertheless, and the architect of a new foreign policy for France which included a firm alliance with Spain. He was in favor of giving away Louisiana in order to cement this friendship. He listened perfunctorily to the impassioned plea of the old man, said a firm no, and dismissed them.

Bienville's step was even slower when they left the Tuileries. "I have very little longer to live," he said to Milhet, as they took their places in the dilapidated carriage, with the Baron as stately as ever on the box, "and now I shall die with the knowledge that my whole life was lived in vain."

Men do not die of broken hearts. Bienville lived for two more years. But they were sad years. The fancy dishes of Renaud seldom tempted him and the Baron spent more time in the courtyard, with his whip over his arm, than in taking his master out for the drives he had once enjoyed so much. In 1768 the founder of New Orleans passed away.

But his life had not been in vain. After a bitter beginning, during which some blood was spilled, the Frenchmen of Louisiana settled down to live under Spanish rule. Later the province was returned to France. Then, always a pawn seemingly, it was sold to the United States by Napoleon Bonaparte when he found himself in need of money. The people at first resented this second transfer as much as they had the first. But in the end the results justified most wonderfully all the vicissitudes through which the colony had suffered and survived.

It is entirely fitting that the final episode in the story of the Mississippi Bubble belongs not to John Law but to the quiet man who spent most of his life in the delta country, holding the mouth of the great river against all aggressors. Although the mad boom of the Bubble was an evil thing, it led in the end to much good. If John Law had not set all France mad with his schemes, the determination to settle the country of the

Mississippi would have been long delayed. Time plays queer tricks on mankind, and it sometimes happens that evil follows in the wake of good. This was a case where the order was reversed, for out of the evils of the Mississippi Bubble came the opening up of the American West. Out of madness came the lasting boom which carried the borders of the United States to the Pacific Ocean.

Index

LANDMARK BOOKS

★